THE QUIET HOUSES -
Fall of the Narcs
Published by Allestone Publications
Copyright © 2022 Jeff Moore

Cover by Reem Al-Baadani
Printed in U.S.A. - 1st Edition

Dedicated to Informant 3071

Contents

CHAPTER 1 - UNEMPLOYED ARTIST

I miss the interesting people more than anything else.

They were the most fascinating people I had ever met. Each more unique, adventurous and flawed than the other. I hated the destruction of their lives but admired their dedication to living in the moment at the expense of everything else. There were never thoughts of tomorrow. They were poor, rich, old, young, violent, friendly, infamous, venturous, selfish and welcoming. They disregarded their differences, their responsibilities, their families for moments to gather in the shadows of unheated basements, alleys, slum apartments, parking lots, street corners, motel rooms and any other place that could camouflage their vices.

I had seen a small sliver of the interesting people in my travels as a street cop in Kansas City, Missouri. I was almost four years into the job that I had only intended to work for a year or two until I was back on my feet as a graphic artist where I belonged and thrived.

After college, I began working as a graphic artist and illustrator in Kansas City where I enjoyed a relaxing job designing food and product packaging for advertising agencies and printing companies. My boss left me alone as I was motivated and talented enough to keep his clients happy. Life moved along in a series of expected moments; career, wife and a new baby.

My suburbanite co-workers and I engaged in daily conversation of hobbies, the Chiefs, the Royals, home chores, weekend projects and nothing much else of substance. It was understood not to bring up politics and our shop was strictly forbidden to discuss anything remotely related to unions. On my first day, I signed a compulsory agreement clause warning if I ever tried to start a union or discussed starting a union, I would be fired on the spot. I guess the rules were easy to follow. Just design food packages and shut the fuck up about unions.

My work was complemented by my small group of lunch associates who were "foodies" before there were actually foodies. Each day was an outing to find an unexplored eatery in Kansas City. Perfectly charred sweet barbecue could be found in dozens of nearby spots with every desirable side dish of comfort food imaginable. Friday was always Mexican food, a 3,000 calorie glutenous meal of authentic southern Mexican cuisine at our favorite spot. Endless chips and salsa was always included.

The routine of my mindless work was always disguised as the creation of laborious artistic masterpieces under the watchful eyes of my boss. He was convinced I was Michelangelo finishing an elaborate marble carving where the slightest misstep would crack a piece of the sculpture onto the floor where I would need to start again. He even refuted requests of our clients as if the small unnecessary requested changes in their designs would diminish my incredible masterpiece or cause me offense. I had a life of comfortable and predictable leisure. I had gained 35 pounds of Mexican Friday lunch fat and even toddled with the idea of home brewing beer as my new hobby.

As my comforting indulgences grew, I became more annoyed by weekly ominous company meetings where the boss discussed some slight changes in the marketplace mood. Each week the meetings and financial winds seemed a little more serious but were quickly dismissed by lunch time. I remember a brief watercolor conversation with Mark, the company accountant who was in charge of basically setting up our fantasy football leagues and not much else.

"Mark, you going to start up the leagues again this year?" I queried.

He delivered a curt response with his hands in his pockets, "Well, I'll be honest with you, the company is insolvent. I'm not really supposed to talk about this but you might want to start to think about popping smoke soon." A month later the doors were closed.

I wasn't as valuable an asset as I had predicted. I was certain Hallmark Cards or a fortune 500 ad agency would have picked me up like a first round draft pick. My talent was stifled as I could only find work in a sweat shop of a printing press company after a two week job search.

The hours were long and the owner was a former Catholic priest who had left the priesthood to manage the company that his brothers had started. The brothers had left the company in his capable hands as they found other financial ventures. Three years later, the priest had flown the company into the side of the mountain without the courtesy of letting the passengers have a complementary drink from the beverage cart. I was out of a job for a second time.

I remember it being very difficult to tell my wife I was now unemployed again, to compound with the stress of taking care of our first baby.

I leafed through the personals of the Kansas City Star where I found a posting for employment with the Kansas City, Missouri Police Department. The carrot was a complementary six month police academy which offered what could be considered a paycheck.

As I sat on a park bench in front of the police headquarters waiting for my entrance interview, a marine in full dress uniform was sitting next to me waiting for his interview as well. We passed greetings and small talk of what it would be like to serve for such a prestigious department.

Without hesitation I will disclose that some of my closest friends and people who I admire as the best and brightest people I've met to this day are part of that department. However, I'll concede there was what I referred to as "the 15%."

Inner city police departments or as some would debase "ghetto departments" have problems with high turnover rates in maintaining recruits due to low pay and work conditions that can possibly lead to an early and violent death. As a result, anyone with a pulse who can do a few push ups and fog a mirror gets through the door. I would conservatively rank 15% of the police recruits as people that I would not trust to make a ham sandwich. A guy in my class had warrants for his arrest and had to clear them up before starting in the academy. Others were an odd assortment of unusual people.

As I sat in a classroom, we were shown over twenty videos of cops being randomly killed while conducting traffic stops or citizen encounters.

A clown next to me rudely interrupted "hey, when are you going to show the ones where the bad guy loses?"

A girl in the class ran out crying and never came back. I started to wonder if I had made questionable decisions in joining the force. The months rolled by and the anxiety built as it came closer to graduation day. We assembled in our dress uniforms before the Chief on the day before graduation.

I can remember in detail a speech given by one of the commanders in the room. "Remember, you are the ones who people look to when they have no one else to turn to. If you can't be the solution, if you can't solve their problems who will those people have to call next, the Army?"

I chuckled in my head as I imagined myself referring a victim of a horrible crime to a nearby Army base and then tipping my hat and exiting with a "Have a nice day."

After the inspiring call to serve speech, our assignments were read aloud. If you were lucky, you were given Central, Metro, North or South Patrol where people somewhat respected the police. If you weren't lucky, you were sent to a place called East Patrol where the streets resembled a Mad Max movie, residents shot each other for fun and hated anything to do with the police. I prepared myself as my name was read, "Officer Jeff Moore—East Patrol."

There were mixed feelings about East Patrol. The young guns or guys looking to become cowboy legends loved that place. There were foot pursuits and car chases every day. You had between 15 and 20 calls per shift and every car had at least one priority shooting or stabbing call per shift. There were drugs and dealers on every street corner. There was never a shortage of crime, bad guys, victims or problems. You never got ahead of the curve and you never really held back the tide for very long.

The old timers in East Patrol had literally seen every sin known to mankind and it showed. This is said with great respect and not exaggerated for effect. They had watched other cops die in the line of duty. They had seen countless people lose their lives from nothing more than the frivolity of bad decisions. They were edgy and dark around the corners. They didn't really trust people anymore. Many drank a lot and couldn't stay married. I learned valuable skills from the old timers I still call upon as a DEA agent today. Sadly, I also felt over time I would eventually become like them, which was concerning. The phrase "ignorance is bliss" is true as I am thankful for the wisdom that comes with experience I now possess but I am burdened by carrying around some of the things I saw during my time at East Patrol.

Each day began with a rowdy sector meeting in a small cinder block walled squad room with eight to ten officers sitting around a table. I was assigned to the afternoon shift from 2:00 p.m. to midnight. Our group had two old timers, Charles Conroy and Martha Bennis. Charles had a distractingly large mustache and an annoying habit of shaking his wrist in order to get his loosely fitted watch to settle upright. Cody, a young guy in the squad would always go at it with Chuck as if he was throwing a rock at a quiet bees' nest hoping to see the ensuing chaos.

I sat in roll-call on my first night as an announcement broadcast over the station speakers, "Any available cars? Shots fired into a residence."

The sergeant at the time, Kenneth Bell shook his head in quiet frustration, "All right guys, they're holding 13 calls in cue so roll call will be short."

Charles politely interrupted the sergeant, "What the hell is the day crew doing boss, sitting on their cherry asses? Sweet Mary n' Joseph."

With a sheepish grin on his face Cody was ready to throw his rock, "Relax Wyatt Earp. You planning on taking down some bad guys tonight?"

The bees' nest erupted, "Son, I was locking up bad guys when your momma was buying your first cap gun at Dollar General. Hell, I probably locked her up shoplifting extra large condoms for her boyfriend Tyreese."

The room violently erupted with childish laughter minus Sgt. Bell's laughter, "All right, enough of that shit. Listen up we've got too many felony warrants in 20 sector. If it gets slow, start looking in the cracks for these guys. If you can't find someone then watch mamma's house. These guys eventually piss off their girlfriends and end up hiding under mamma's skirt. Wear your body armor tonight. I don't care how fucking hot it is."

Grown adults with the lives of human beings in their hands gathered around a table making middle school mom jokes. That's how it went, day after day, year after year and so on. Sgt. Bell ushered his children into the warm evening air with his usual words of caution. "All right get out there and be safe."

During my probationary training I rode with Chuck most of the time. When he was off, Martha would fill in as the field training officer. The new guys always got the "whip" or the junk car. My car had 243,000 miles on it. We all drove a Ford Crown Victoria and mine was a rebuild made from two other salvaged police cars. The front end of a wrecked car had been welded to the back end of another salvaged car. It was never washed or cleaned. The backseat was beyond filthy. It topped out at 80 so we were never much use in the car chases.

Martha and Chuck were like parents who locked up the liquor cabinet because they knew if they weren't around you would end up in a coma. They were good people and they knew how easy it was to make a mistake that you couldn't recover from. I tried my best not piss them off and embarrass myself.

Chuck hated the management. In his mind, he'd been unfairly passed over for promotions and "wrongly" disciplined for his acts of valor that didn't go perfectly as planned. He wanted to retire at the first possible moment. I resented his negative attitude at times but I listened to any advice he would share to help me stay out of harm's way. He pointed out some of the problem people in our sector to me. He demonstrated the way to spot a person carrying a concealed firearm just by the way they walked. He lectured on how to spot a dope house and a person on the corner who was holding a bag of dope. He would always warn me that the most dangerous guy in the room is the guy who has nothing to lose.

About a quarter of the recruits ended up washing out or just leaving the job. Some had visions of their job resembling a TV police drama show with handsome beautiful people solving compelling tidy mysteries.

As a recruit, you're volunteered for any call high stress call involving murder, mayhem or a stinker (a dead body) during your probationary period. I was volunteered on my third day to help with a crime scene involving a shooting. No heavy lifting, just put up some crime scene tape and keep people from walking through it. Two drug dealers were shot execution style behind an apartment building with one gentleman's head missing about a quarter of the front portion of his skull. The blood from one of the bodies was pooling in the curb of the street leading into the complex. I watched as the pool of blood became so large that it began to escape and run down the street. The fire department was kind enough to arrive and do a great wash down of the pavement.

I had never seen a murdered person before this. I stared at the bodies for three hours without blinking or looking away. I memorized every detail in their clothing, their shoes and their final frozen expressions on their faces. It was impersonal and quiet. No one seemed to be alarmed around me and absolutely no one cared. It was as if this was an expected and socially accepted situation. I did my best to pretend that it didn't bother me and I had been there before. I needed to blend in at East Patrol.

A recruit from my class was transferred to my squad and was assigned to ride with Martha. His name was Brandon and he wasn't making the marks needed to get off probation. He wasn't comfortable with talking to people on the street and lacked what is described in our training as "command presence." I liked Brandon but I think he worried too much about offending people. He came from the banking sector where you conduct yourself a little differently than on the streets of East Patrol. Martha was tough on the recruits and didn't have a problem with firing people. This is probably why they gave Brandon to her.

Chuck and I were traveling in the whip when a call came across the radio, "Dispatch to three-fourteen."

I grabbed the radio and responded with my location to let the dispatcher know I could take the call, "Three-fourteen at 23rd and Van Brunt."

"Three-fourteen, respond to an intoxicated party down in the area of Truman and Paseo," the dispatcher relayed.

Before I could respond to the dispatcher, I heard Martha's deep gravelly voice over the radio, "Dispatch, show three-twelve on the call with three-fourteen for training and as the primary car."

Poor Brandon. He was now the primary officer for this call and I was his backup car. As much as Chuck annoyed me with his complaining I thanked the God of field training officers I had not been assigned as Martha's probationary officer.

Chuck and I arrived first but waited in the car for a few minutes for Brandon to arrive. I could see a row of slum apartments that were home to mostly drug addicts and other destitute people living in that area. I saw our distressed citizen who was deep in slumber leaning against a tree next to the apartment building with his legs sprawled apart and partially blocking the sidewalk.

He was a local problem transient who lived on the streets passing his time by pissing off as many people as he could during the day. His left arm was clutched around a cheap box of wine. Until this call, I didn't know that wine was actually sold in boxes. He was shirtless and I could see a large tattoo across his stomach where the words "momma tried" were written in an old English font. His skin was leathery and deeply tanned from spending most of his time outdoors. He was motionless and I hoped he was deceased in order to spare Brandon the humiliation he would soon endure. I was certain that he was insanely intoxicated and would not appreciate Brandon's gentle polite attempts to wake him up.

Brandon finally arrived and quickly exited his vehicle. He was breathing hard and I could tell he was nervous.

Chuck was lighting up a cigarette and spoke first, "Hi Martha, he looks like he's taking a nap."

"Thanks Chuck, the newbie is having problems with his geography. It took us a little longer to get here than expected," Martha smugly responded.

The recruits were also evaluated on arrival times to calls and expected to know the areas they patrolled. This was before GPS devices and you were expected to memorize your beat. Most of us drove the neighborhoods on our days off to help learn the geography faster in order to impress our field training officers.

Brandon began to slowly approach the slumbering man in an overly cautious manner. Martha quickly interrupted, "What are we forgetting to do now Brandon?"

Brandon fumbled with his lapel radio mic, "Um, this is 312. Myself and 314, we're ten-seven making contact with the party down."

Martha was not impressed, "All right Brandon, you're in charge. What's next?"

My job on this call was easy. I just had to watch Brandon's back while he made contact with the intoxicated party. Brandon cautiously and slowly moved closer to the man. Brandon kept one hand tightly on his holstered weapon in the event career street drunk was actually a Navy Seal feigning a nap to gain tactical advantage before disarming the police.

Chuck yawned while simultaneously exhaling cigarette smoke,

"This should be interesting, Jeff." I remained patiently quiet as I really didn't want to add to Brandon's stress level.

In an uncomfortably forced voice, Brandon yelled into the man's face, "Sir! I am a police officer! Do you need medical treatment?" Everyone seemed surprised at the volume Brandon was able to muster from his meek demeanor. There was no response.

From nowhere, a boisterous voice yelled, "Hey dumb ass, check his dick for a pulse. He may be dead!"

The unexpected vulgarity startled me as I turned to see a very heavy set black woman who had issued the proclamation to Brandon. She was standing behind us 15 feet away or more on the sidewalk. I could tell she wasn't a threat but she was another layer of crap to deal with on the call. I now had to watch her to make sure she wouldn't interrupt whatever the hell Brandon was trying to do. She had short hair that had been partially died blond at one time but was returning to its natural color. She wore a large baggy dirty t-shirt that covered her robust frame. She had an interesting face that seemed friendly, funny and wise all at the same time. In the corner of her smiling mouth was a thin Black and Mild cigar. She casually drew smoke from the cigar and exhaled the smoke from her nostrils. Her name, I would later learn, was Tamera Josephine Mack as we would eventually cross paths again. She knew everyone on the streets and was simply known as "Big Tammy" or "T." For now, she was just the annoying wise cracking by-stander turning Brandon's citizen contact into outdoor theatre performance art for all to enjoy.

Brandon's courage level increased as he was now shaking the man's shoulder to rouse him. The man's eyes blinked open slowly as he intoxicatedly stared up into the sky.

His voice was croaky and soaked with the odor of alcohol as he belted, "Yes sir, I'm a decorated combat veteran. Did you know that son? I bet you didn't."

Brandon seemed confused by the questions and mentally fumbled for his next response, "How are you sir, do you need an ambulance?" The man simply ignored Brandon and closed his eyes again as if returning to his natural state of perpetual sleep.

Martha's face looked stern but more patient than usual, "Frisk him, grab his ID and let's run him for warrants."

Brandon did as he was told. I moved closer in the event my assistance would be needed. Tammy remained quiet but waited patiently watching Brandon. As Brandon ran his hands over the pockets and the waistband of the man to check for a weapon, he opened his eyes again.

He slowly removed a packaged condom from his pocket and offered it to Brandon as if it was his identification, "Here you go, kid." The man glanced at Martha's face which was now flushed red, "Go fuck yourself and your fat momma." The man coarsely laughed at his delivered insult to Brandon and Martha.

In response, Brandon abruptly yelled louder, "I need your identification now, sir!" I knew it was useless to talk further to this man. It was "hands on" time now. The man began to lean towards the nozzle on the box of wine in a lethargic attempt to get it to his mouth.

Chuck had grown impatient and flicked his cigarette to the ground, "May I, Martha?"

"Go ahead, Chuck," she responded. It was now time to go "old school" with the drunk.

Chuck knelt down next to him and grabbed the man's dirty blonde beard with a tightly closed grip.

The man yelled in pain, "Hey what the hell, man?"

Chuck refused to release his grip and simply increased the pain level to demand his full attention, "I'm a combat veteran, too. What's your rank and where did you serve?" I had never heard Chuck mention military service in our conversations so I was not sure if this was true on his part.

"My name is Mike Taylor and I know my rights, mother fucker," screamed the man.

Chuck used his freehand to feel around Taylor's socks and was able to fish out a small pocket knife. In an impressive move, Chuck used one hand to flick the knife open before offering his advice, "Brandon, always treat everyone as if they're armed and dangerous. Start patting down a person at their waist but don't forget to check shoes. You might find dope there too."

Brandon mentally took in the advice and hoped in his mind that missing the knife on the frisk would not be another card stacked against him or possibly get him thrown from the program.

Taylor belted loudly, "That knife is legal you son of a bitch! You got no right to take that!"

Chuck ignored his legal demands and handed the knife to Brandon. I removed my cuffs from my belt and cuffed the man's hands behind his back as Chuck released his grip on his beard.

Chuck addressed Brandon with instructions, "Brandon, cut a hole in the wine box."

Tammy's eyes widened in excitement as she removed the cigar from the corner of her mouth. All of us except Brandon had an idea of the ramifications of taking a transient drunk man's box of wine and pouring it out in front of him. Brandon leaned forward with the knife preparing to puncture the side of the box.

Mike pleaded for mercy for his companion, the wine box, "Hey son, I was just messing with you. I'll leave. Or you can arrest me if you want. Just don't pour out my wine. Don't do this to a veteran, son. I served my country for you."

Brandon had reached his threshold for stupidity as well. He aggressively plunged the knife into the box. He seemed content and somewhat pleased with his actions. Maybe he imagined the box of wine was Martha's exposed back. As the wine quickly gushed out of the box, Mike Taylor exploded into a writhing toddler screaming and rolling on the ground. He buried his face into the waterfall of escaping wine until his face was covered and completely purple. No one really stopped him as it seemed too cruel at that point. We all let him drink as much as he could capture before the box ran dry.

We called for a prisoner transport van that was used to transport belligerent prisoners or people who could not be restrained in the back of a patrol car to get Mr. Taylor off the sidewalk and downtown for a quick booking on misdemeanor intoxication charges.

Brandon was extended on his probation for an additional three weeks but did finally make it off probation with Martha's concurrence.

CHAPTER 2 - THE ROOKIE

I was finished with probation and had left the safe protective nests of Martha and Chuck. I was on my own to some extent or at least more accountable for my actions now that I was off probation.

I was occasionally allowed to ride as a one person car if there was availability with our squad's vehicles. Each squad had four or five cars. The majority of the time you rode with a second officer as a two person crew. Some calls didn't require a second officer such as vehicular accidents, taking theft reports from a business or if someone's house had been burglarized and there were no suspects on scene. You were always encouraged to call for a second car if the need arose. If you were a one person crew, you often had to respond to the lobby of the station as many people came in person to report crimes instead of calling for the police and waiting for the police to arrive. It was not unusual for people to drive to the police station who had brought someone in their car who needed medical attention from an assault. I had been dispatched on one occasion when a female shooting victim was brought to the East Patrol visitor lot by her friend. I arrived and found the woman hysterical as her friend had already passed away.

The most senior veteran of the squad was always given the newest car in the group as some sort of reward for service. Each squad also had a prisoner van for transporting prisoners which was referred simply as a "wagon." There were four squads at East Patrol which meant at any given time there were four wagons in service. When you volunteered to drive the wagon you were expected not initiate proactive stops so that the wagon was always available for "pick-ups." Your primary job as a wagon driver was transporting and picking up belligerent arrests or people who couldn't be transported inside of a patrol car. Occasionally, if it was extremely busy, a wagon would be dispatched as a second car on a call. Wagons were great if you had a person who was, for a lack of a better description, not clean, which was most of the time. There was usually a guy or two in each group who was retired on duty. They preferred not to do proactive policing, instead volunteering to permanently to be the squad's wagon driver. I found it hard to believe some people wanted to become police officers and then volunteered to become a permanent taxi service for prisoners.

It was busy throughout most of our shifts on any given day and it was unbearably busy in the summertime. A lot of people didn't have the most comfortable living arrangements during the hot months of the year and the agitations and disagreements were exasperated by the heat.

The majority of our calls were assaults involving domestic violence. Domestic violence had a broad umbrella which covered more than just people who were married or related by blood but also included people who resided together as roommates. You were always required as an officer to make an arrest if a physical assault had occurred. The system was not capable of handling the sheer volume of people simply beating on each other every day. I had arrested a man for assaulting his wife early in my shift on one occasion. He was released from jail before my shift had ended and we were actually dispatched to his residence for a second domnestic assault during the same shift where he was again arrested. It was sadly comical how flawed and failed the system was.

Our squad covered an area referred to as "20 Sector" which had a higher level of homicides than other parts of Kansas City. We normally had at least one homicide per week in our area.

Early on in my time at East Patrol, Chuck and I were dispatched late in the evening on a call regarding shots fired inside of a residence. We arrived and parked our car short of the residence by a house or two. It was procedure to never park directly in front of your dispatched location or to pass your location. This was a safer approach where you could exit your car without the possibility of a sudden ambush and to make your approach more cautiously.

There was snow on the ground and we could see footprints from people who had left the house prior to our arrival. It was unusually quiet and the front door of the house was open. We called for a second car and were assisted by two additional officers and a supervisor who also arrived on scene.

We drew our weapons and entered the dark house with our flashlights to search for injured people. There was a younger deceased white male subject on the floor in a hallway between the living room and a bedroom. A section of his skull towards the top crown part of his head had been blown away from a gunshot that had entered under his chin. As I crept past his body to continue clearing the house, I could feel my boot slightly glide through the gore on the floor that had expelled from his head.

The story of his demise, I learned, was more senseless than others. The victim was a parolee who had been released from prison two months earlier. He was with his best friend at the house with three other people celebrating. His friend was smoking a cigar or cigarette which had been dipped in a liquid drug called PCP. Cigarettes dipped in PCP were sold on the street for $20 a piece. Some dealers carried bottles of PCP and allowed customers to dip their own cigarettes into the bottles. PCP is an incredibly strong hallucinogenic drug that alters sensory perception, mood and thought patterns. It often leads a person to bizarre, violent and psychotic behavior.

The victim's friend was carrying a pistol on his person when he arrived at the house and began to smoke. While smoking his "dipped" cigarette, he pulled his firearm from his waistband and began shooting wildly inside of the residence, hitting his friend and not injuring anyone else. The remaining occupants fled from the house and left the area. When the suspect was located and arrested, he had no memory of killing his friend. The addicts inside the residence were witnesses at his trial and corroborated how the events unfolded as described.

PCP was a scary thing on the street. It turned people into absolute zombies and gave some unbelievable strength and brutality. It, unfortunately, and unnecessarily, led to many fatal encounters with officers.

I was lucky and had only been involved in one shooting during my brief time at East Patrol. I was riding alone as a one person crew and was dispatched to "40 Sector," an area outside of my own. It covered the Southeast section of East Patrol's territory. The call was at a house in a blue collar residential suburb which was usually quiet and didn't have many calls for service. I was dispatched with another one person car which was sent from another area outside of 40 Sector. I arrived first and after my second car arrived, we made contact with a gentleman at the door of his house. He indicated to us his wife had been depressed and asked if we could come inside and speak with her.

The other officer and I followed the man into his kitchen and saw his wife sitting at the kitchen table. She was blankly staring at the wall across from her and would not make eye contact with myself or the other officer. She was wearing a baggy sweatshirt and her right forearm was out of view tucked under her sweatshirt.

I approached her and introduced myself in a gentle voice as not to startle her. She continued to stare at the wall ignoring my presence. I leaned towards her to ask her name in a calm quiet voice which I thought was appropriate for the situation.

The man was extremely nervous and was smoking to calm his nerves. I partially turned my head towards him to listen to him speak as he casually announced to the room,"Hey just to let you guys know, she might have my handgun, I can't find it anywhere."

I immediately knew without having to receive any additional information she was armed with his handgun and was holding it under her shirt. I also knew I was now disadvantaged as my head was turned away from her listening to the man speak. She had planned a "suicide by cop" scenario with her husband acting as an unwitting accomplice.

As I turned my attention back to her, the race had already begun. Her hand was secured to the grip of the handgun she was pulling from her waistband. I could see it was almost free from concealment with the muzzle now becoming visible.

The man was screaming for us not to kill her and went as so far as to grab my partner's arm as he tried to draw his firearm. They became engaged in a loud scuffle behind me. I lacked enough time to pull my weapon from my holster and instead grabbed as much of her firearm as I could with both of my hands as she pulled the weapon free. I was fortunate, able to wrap all of the fingers of my left hand around the barrel. My right hand wrapped tightly around her hand that was holding the grip of the weapon. I was able to control the barrel enough to keep it from pointing anywhere towards myself, however she was controlling the trigger of the weapon and would decide when the firearm would discharge. She attempted to stand up with a strong kick of her legs I had not anticipated.

She started to rise from the chair and I could feel the weapon increasing its twisting torquing pressure in my hand. I gave her a shoulder to keep her off balanced enough to prevent her from standing up completely. However, she refused to diminish the strength of her grip on the firearm. As she lost her balance and fell back to a seated position, the weapon discharged loudly as her finger had inadvertently squeezed the trigger. She immediately released the weapon and violently jerked her body knocking us both over onto the floor. The round had entered her pelvic area and exited through the side of her thigh missing my leg. My ears rang but I knew the worst was over as I had her gun in my left hand and had my duty weapon in my right. It was strange as there was not one single drop of blood. It was a meaty flesh wound with not much else. She was treated for the gunshot, received treatment for her depression and as far as I know moved on from that experience.

I found the first two years of East Patrol exciting, surreal but also concerning and at times upsetting from the levels of havoc. By the third year I had far less tolerance from continuously watching people suffer and die from making bad decisions.

There were a lot of young guys at East Patrol who loved the excitement and chaos. There were even a rare few who invited the opportunity of someday getting to use their firearm in an actual gunfight. The neighborhoods of East Patrol didn't seem to mind at all. In fact, it seemed as if the neighborhoods invited the challenge calling out "come explore us and see if we let you leave." Some guys thrived in the lawlessness and others weren't as lucky.

I distanced myself from the guys who were making questionable decisions and tried to steer people on a straighter course when it was possible or needed. Some guys were empowered by their authority and didn't feel the need to answer to anyone.

A buddy of mine thought it would be okay to personally requisition $500 from a Friday night drunk driving arrest. His arrest was a belligerent idiot working on his third DUI for which my friend believed the theft of his cash was justified and a further lesson learned. A state prosecutor disagreed and charged the officer with armed robbery since the money was technically taken under threat by firearm the officer possessed but never removed from his duty holster. He was given eight years in Jefferson City Correctional Center.

My time in patrol went by quickly. I learned the ropes, solicited respected veterans for their advice and learned my beat. I knew the people who were the problems and which people genuinely needed my help. My arrests were solid and most ended up with convictions without being tossed by a prosecutor for a bad or sloppy stop. I felt like I was part of the solution. Still, I felt there was more to experience.

I began to form an interest of a specific group of people on the streets who were more deliberate and organized with their decisions and activities. These people at times lived violently but also worked to minimize risks when possible. They moved more at night and sought to be less conspicuous when possible during the day. These people were the dealers, the dope pushers of the neighborhoods.

They were uneducated in academics but excelled in other skill sets essential to their existence. They relied upon the ability to read other people as their most important method of their survival. They constantly asked themselves, "Will this person try to kill me, rob me, let me rob them, buy my dope at an inflated price, sell bad dope to me or snitch me to the police?" The dealers who could play the odds and guess the outcome of these questions were the ones who lasted longer and moved up through the ranks over the others.

In almost twenty years of working drug cases I've reached the verdict that there are really only three types of drug traffickers. There are the people at the bottom who sell grams, bindles and baggies. At the next level are the guys who move ounces of dope and at the top are the big players at the kilogram levels. Everyone wants to move up. It's a game. The younger players moving ounces are the most violent and have the most to lose. They're usually in their early 20s and are learning the game and what works. A lot of the lower level dealers are drug addicts themselves working to support their habits. As a road cop, you deal mostly with the guys (and gals) at the bottom of the ladder and once in a while you get lucky with someone holding a bigger bag of dope.

These people exhaustingly fascinated me. I had not seen anything like it before. They had no masters and answered to no one. They didn't pay taxes. They didn't clock in at work. They returned calls only when it was convenient or suited them to do so. They had cars, jewelry, guns, women, cash, indiscreet places to stay and play. They moved quietly each day throughout the streets growing more influential in their neighborhoods. They enslaved and poisoned minds without guilt. Their world was secret and the worst part is they could see you before you saw them.

I wanted to learn this game and work narcotics cases but I needed someone to deal me in at the table. There were two narcotics squads within the department but they were difficult to get promoted to. Some guys worked their entire careers and were unable to make it to a drug squad.

I had a good friend who could possibly give me a hand up or at least tell me if it was worth the effort. His name was Roderick Clay but everyone called him Country. He was liked by everybody. He was funny and he was relaxed. Everything came easy to him. On his second year on the job, he had been in an actual car chase with bank robbers shooting at him, like something from a movie. One of the bullets had penetrated his vehicle traveling through the engine compartment and lodged with the very tip of the bullet peeking through the plastic of the cruiser dashboard. The bullet appeared as if it was peeking into the front seat area of Country's police cruiser. He had been promoted from South Patrol to the Street Narcotics Unit (or simply called SNU by everyone).

SNU was a small reclusive group of undercover police officers referred to as "narcs" who kept to themselves. They worked from a small windowless basement office rented out of a warehouse in downtown Kansas City which was referred to as "the cave." There were eight narcs who worked for Sgt. Ryan Shale, the supervisor of SNU.

They had one mission. They were tasked with dismantling or shutting down as many "nuisance" houses as possible. The police brass refused to use denigrative terms like "drug house" or "crack house." Instead, the term "nuisance house" was employed. There were thousands of "nuisance houses" but not a single drug house in Kansas City, Missouri.

Sgt. Shale arrived to SNU in 1998. He was handed the ropes after the prior SNU supervisor was promoted to a captain over the night shift at Metro Patrol.

Shale seemed a natural fit. He was a worker and never slowed down. He had four "good shootings" under his belt, had arrested more bad guys, seized more dope and guns off the street than anyone else around him. He was divorced without much of a personal life. He lived and breathed police work and he had little tolerance for people who couldn't follow his lifestyle. He was trusted by the police leadership to put up impressive stats while not embarrassing the department in the process.

One afternoon he was called to the office of the Chief of Police unexpectedly for a casual sit down. He arrived early in his dress uniform which was always required for a sit down with the chief even if it was described as a "completely casual" sit down. He found his way to the ornately furnished office on the top floor of the downtown police headquarters building.

Despite using glued together wrecked police cars, the KCMO PD spared no expense to ensconce the chief's office with ornate trappings and accolades of adornment. Shale had never seen the temple of leadership and took in the impressive sights in the event he would not be able to return there again. Shale was greeted politely by the Chief's assistant and led into his office.

Shale deliberately removed his hat only when in front of Chief Bryan McColley as a visual cue of respect. The chief, was nondescript in appearance apart from for a large discolored "whiskey nose" in the center of his face.

Bryan quickly greeted Shale, "Ryan, thanks for dropping by. I'd like you to meet a friend of ours. This is Mike Portelli. He's the department attorney and a close friend of a few guys on the bench across the street. He's a good person to know."

Shale gave his best 10 dollar handshake to the department attorney while his mind raced with visions of impending lawsuits to the department as a result of his wild ventures.

Mike commenced with the pleasantries to break the ice in the room, "My hats off to you guys putting yourself in harms way out there. The chief tells me you're his best crime fighter."

Shale did his best to appear modest. "I've got a great team of hard-working guys. I just take the credit."

Everyone seated themselves comfortably and waited for the Chief to speak, "As you might have heard, the mayor is getting some bad press on the numbers. We've had an increase in drug related homicides to the tune of 12% since this time last year. A local golf pro's wife was found overdosed in an inner city drug house two weeks ago which has helped to put a bright light on the city's growing drug problem. We don't have the resources right now to deal with this and honestly the mayor looks like he's sitting on his thumbs."

Mike waited for his cue to provide more details, "Currently, Jackson County doesn't have the bed space to house drug offenders. The jail is running at almost double capacity. Most of the felony drug cases involving amounts under 100 grams are pled down to probation, maybe 90 days in jail at best. The short version is we've got room to hold the murderers and rapists but not the dope pushers. It's a revolving door for those guys."

Shale now relieved the meeting wasn't about some disciplinary issue focused on the problem at hand and asked, "What options do we have?"

The Chief responded, "We've talked to police chiefs in other cities with the same issues to get some ideas of what works. From what we've learned, if we focus more on problem nuisance houses as opposed to street corner drug sales, it has a bigger visual impact in the community."

"How's that, sir?" Ryan asked without trying to appear he already knew the answer to his own question.

The chief responded to Shale's question, "What looks better; the optics of arresting four people on street corners for selling bags of dope, or closing four nuisance houses? And for the coup de grâce, I'll concede to Mike."

Mike let out a pleasant but nervous chuckle. "I know this is a big ask, but we'd like to see the utilization of more undercover officers as opposed to only using informants on these nuisance houses. I know this isn't what you might want to hear but the cases are much stronger and juries and judges would rather see cops on the stand when presenting evidence."

A pause hung in the air until the Chief spoke, "What are you thinking, Ryan?"

Shale knew the Chief and Mike were clueless on this issue and wouldn't know what a bag of crack rocks looked like if it was sitting in their laps so he was careful to choose his words. "These places are incredibly toxic filled with people who have nothing to lose. On a good day it takes two or three minutes for our tactical unit to extract an informant and we're not always successful in getting them out safely. Look, it's like this, informants are like disposable lighters. They have their purpose, they work great but when they're used up, you just grab a new one. And if you lose a lighter or you break one, it's just a lighter."

Everyone knew without having to bring it to the surface further that if an informant was killed in a drug house, it was an inconvenience and a little bit of paperwork. Not so much the case if a narc met the same fate. Unfortunately, Shale had made up his mind. He knew that if he couldn't deliver, then it was a sign of not meeting the Chief's expectations. Supervisors in privileged positions who failed to meet expectations of the Chief of Police sometimes found themselves in new positions as instructors at the police academy or managing a supply closet somewhere. Shale reversed his course and assured the chief and Mike that his narcs would step up their game and fulfill the task.

Shale returned to his office where he debriefed Alice, the SNU administrative assistant on the chief's request. Alice worked for SNU preparing "tip sheets" which were leads called into the police tip lines about active drug houses. Sometimes just an address was given and sometimes a name or phone number was provided. Alice prepared each tip sheet for the narcs.

Shale's dark humor led him to purchase a brightly painted glass Mexican el Día de los Muertos skull with an opening centered at the top of the skull. Shale would roll up each tip sheet with a rubber band and then stick the sheets into the hole at the top of the skull. The papers stuck out of the top like wild hair. Shale would then pass it around to the narcs in the room who would each randomly in turn select their tip sheets. Shale loved this method of random fate. He felt a sense of relief as he would not be responsible for anyone's choices of picking a dangerous or possibly fatal drug house. It was all in the hands of the skull. He was removed from the culpability of the process.

Alice hated her job. She worried eventually she would prepare a tip sheet leading to the demise of a narc. Shale had once threatened her with termination when he discovered she occasionally "round filed" the tips she felt were too dangerous to be assigned to the narcs.

She mustered the courage to voice her displeasure with the new bar set by the chief, "The guys aren't going to like this, Ryan, and I particularly don't either."

"Well, Alice, they all want the beards, long hair, cool guy tatts playing dope man doing the easy corner buys. They've gotten too comfortable.

They all choose to be here and we have a job to do. Do you have the sheets ready for this week?" he asked.

Alice had finished rolling up the pieces of paper and carefully handed them to Shale as he retrieved the skull from a cabinet.

As the skull came into her view she cringed, "I hate this fucking thing."

Shale laughed at her disgust and rare use of profanity, "There's a fine line between insanity and genius. I've erased that line."

For myself, the process of joining SNU began with a beer and friendly conversation with Country. I expected him to throw cold water on our conversation but he was supportive. He answered my questions and didn't make any promises. I was told I would have to pass "the test," whatever that was, and show my interest to Shale by participating on some "ride-a-longs" and hanging out at the cave once in a while.

Country told me most of the guys only stayed for a year or two at SNU and then left for other units. I scoffed at that idea and proudly informed him that there was no way I could leave a job like that unless they fired me.

He smirked and would only say, "You'll have to see for yourself when you get there."

I informed him I was ready, to which he responded it was important I knew what I was getting into. He explained that it was an intense exciting job but he was going back to the field soon. He had been at SNU for a year and a half and that was enough excitement for him. If I could do the things he had mentioned, pass the test with flying colors, then Country would vouch for me with Shale.

I knew this would be the only shot I would get, so I went overboard, as I usually do with most endeavors. I went on dozens of ride-a-longs. I brought in pizza and subs for the narcs once in a while if they had a late night. If they needed a uniformed officer and a marked patrol car for an operation or prisoner transport, I was on the spot to volunteer no matter the time of day or night or on the weekend. I had no self respect in my groveling. Shale never once gave me the time of day or even a polite nod. Hopefully, he noticed my efforts.

With the day of the narc test approaching, I signed the applicant list with 11 other guys. The test was really simple and didn't require a number two pencil. You pulled a tip sheet from Shale's skull, knocked on the door of a staged drug house, talked your way inside, bought some faux dope and left. It seemed simple enough but with Shale, nothing came simple or without sacrifice.

Shale had staged his narcs as actors inside of his "drug" house where he borrowed a sawed off shotgun from the evidence vault and loaded it with blank shells. The narcs took the test a little too serious and didn't tolerate anyone breaking character. If you got snappy, cocky or gave an unacceptable answer to one of their questions or demands, one of the narcs in the house blasted you with the shotgun. Other than shitting your pants, permanent hearing loss and the department wide broadcast news of failing the SNU test, there were no other adverse affects to this testing process.

Shale brought in legendary retired SNU alumni, Scott Skinner who was the lead actor of the scenario based test. Scott was bar none, the best narc who had worked at SNU. He had knocked hundreds of doors and gotten into the hardest and most violent houses in the city. He made more undercover drug buys than any other narc who had come through the unit. It was almost worth taking the test just to see him in action. He had a quiet demeanor, short stature and looked a little bit like Eminem.

I passed the test but wasn't sure if I had really impressed anyone. I did, however, leave the house without the shotgun going off and had a 10 dollar piece of soap resembling crack cocaine in my hand. I was ranked number four on the applicant list. The number three guy on the list was promoted to sergeant and taken off the list. A girl in the number two spot on the list became pregnant and was removed from the list. By unexpected departures of the other applicants, I was rapidly moving my way closer to SNU.

When I received the call informing me I was transferring to SNU, Chuck and I were on a call involving a "stinker" found along the railroad tracks in a part of East Patrol referred to as "the bottoms." The area was just south of the Missouri River near East Front Street and west of Interstate 435. The area had a few houses but was mostly factories, truck stops and manufacturing plants.

A railroad cop called it in. It wasn't our area but we got the call when no one in the sector to the North of us was available. We arrived and met our contact who gave us his information and took us to the body. The location of the body was near a large railroad yard. There were transient tent camps 200 yards away from where the body lay in a lightly wooded area.

The camps belonged to homeless people who rode and jumped on the trains between cities or even across the entire country. They would camp and stay for days or weeks before jumping a train leaving the area.

The people I had met there once before were from California. The people in the camps were usually quiet, kept to themselves, so we really didn't have much contact with them unless there was an assault or something like this.

Chuck was happy the body was found early in our shift. Normally a natural deceased person or a homicide scene takes up your entire shift. You have to remain with the body while the Crime Scene Unit processes the area around the body and the county mortician arrives and retrieves the body. Chuck loved calls like this where he could stand around, smoke cigarettes for hours and tell recycled stories while I was forced to listen with no avenue of escape.

The body was a white male in his mid 60's, if I had to guess. He was lying on his side with his eyes closed. I didn't see any blood or signs of trauma. I could tell he was a transient train hopper by looking at his shoes. His toes were almost poking out of the large holes in the soles of his well worn shoes and his hands were calloused and dirty.

Chuck tried to launch into another story but I was saved by a phone call from Country who shared the news of my new assignment. Country had vouched for me with Shale, informing Shale he would personally train me. I thanked Country and assured him I would not embarrass him and would learn the job quickly. I remember Country laughing at my response before he ended the call.

I was on my way to becoming a narc and finally getting to see how the sausage was made. Chuck was genuinely happy for me to get out of East Patrol for a while and stretch my legs. I thanked him for his free sage advice over the years and told him I would keep in contact with him to share my exploits. He shook his wrist to settle his watch to his liking, as he did a hundred times a day before extinguishing his cigarette.

CHAPTER 3 - PANCHO

Pancho was a 6 foot tall black man of a medium and slightly muscled build. His hair and goatee were flecked in color with slight early graying. He was in his early 30's but carried himself as if he were a much older man with the wisdom of much more experienced person. He always moved in a deliberately calm relaxed manner never moving too quickly or too slow as to bring unnecessary attention to his presence. He was polite, unusually quiet and spoke only when responding to another person's question or initiation of a conversation.

Pancho grew up in southern California. His now deceased father was a ranking member of the Gangster Disciples in Los Angeles. When Pancho was 15, his father tasked him with taking a train from Los Angeles to Little Rock, Arkansas with a pound of heroin concealed in his back pack. When Pancho arrived, he was arrested attempting to deliver the heroin to a drug informant working for the state police.

Pancho spent the next 4 years in a juvenile offender program. By obligating himself to join the military as an adult he was given early supervised release status with an expunged criminal record of his arrest as a juvenile. Pancho served in the Army and was deployed to Afghanistan as part of Operation Enduring Freedom after the 9-11 Twin Tower attacks. Pancho returned to Fort Riley near Junction City, Kansas City in 2003 but made his way to visit Antonio Hill in Kansas City, Missouri for a brief business endeavor.

Antonio was a stocky black man in his mid 40's with a full beard and unusually light colored eyes. He was covered in ornate dark tattoos for which he spared no expense to find the best artists, traveling as far as to Japan and Australia to employ his favorite skin artists. Antonio had a comforting funny falsetto laugh and an easy sense of humor which was rarely vulgar. His demeanor often caused people to forget how dangerous of a person he actually was. Antonio had grown up in housing projects, foster homes and the squalid floors of drug houses throughout the city. His only remaining link to humanity was his care and devotion of a handicapped sister, Karina, who he loved immensely.

He was a very successful cocaine and heroin trafficker who had built his organization to the point of being able to comfortably distribute 10-15 kilograms per week. On the street, Antonio was known by his nickname, Red, which was also the name of his front business, a barbecue restaurant located in Blue Springs, Missouri.

The drugs were shipped to Red once or twice a month from Arizona in vehicles with fabricated concealed compartments built into their frames. The vehicles were loaded with bricks of compressed cocaine and heroin tightly packaged in layers of tape, plastic, carbon paper and grease. The components of the drug packaging layers were used in an attempt to reduce the detection of odors to a police drug dog. Each brick resembled a large book wrapped in tape and weighed exactly one kilogram. The outside of the bricks were also artistically marked in a way to discourage anyone from opening the bricks and then trying to reseal the packaging to its original form. If any of the markings on the packaging were tampered or altered, the entire shipment was sent back to Arizona unused. This would usually culminate with the punishment of any person who had been found to have altered or opened the narcotics during its shipment to Kansas City.

The vehicles were loaded onto car hauler trucks and trailers through legitimate freight transport companies. The drivers of the car hauler trucks were unaware of the contraband inside of the vehicles. The load cars were always transported across country without license plates or visible way to identify the registration of the vehicle during the trip.

Upon arrival to Kansas City, the vehicles were usually unloaded in a visible public parking lot such as a Home Depot, Lowes or a Walmart in the middle of the day, never at night. Red knew hiding in plain sight was the best camouflage of criminal activity that there was. If you unloaded a vehicle in a dark alleyway at three in the morning, it was obvious you were doing something illegal. If you unloaded a car in a public parking lot with the confidence of someone simply picking up a new car in front of the cops and the world to see, it was nothing of importance.

Red's customers were large drug traffickers in their own right who normally purchased five to ten bricks at a time from Red. These wholesale dealers in turn broke their drugs down further for street level distribution. Red did not like to sell less than three of four bricks on any given transaction. If you were unable to move this amount of dope, then you were wasting Red's time and would need to go somewhere else for your product.

Red had people in his organization who were tasked with one specific job and were never asked to do anything other than that job. Many of his employees were unaware of the other people working for Red within the same organization. Pancho was hired only to kill other drug dealers, people who stole from Red or suspected informants on the street and nothing else. He had no other purpose and was not introduced to any other member of the Red's crew.

Desean Hill was Antonio's cousin. He was the only person ever allowed under any circumstance to handle the arriving drug shipments on the car hauler trucks. At any given time, Desean had burner phones that he bought by the dozen. Desean coordinated the shipping of the load vehicles with people in Arizona. Antonio never spoke on the phone regarding the shipments and would always meet with Desean at his restaurant to receive updates and arrival times of the shipments.

When a load car arrived on a truck, Desean met the driver of the transport and took possession of the vehicle. Desean would place a license plate on the vehicle and drive it to a parking lot of an apartment building where the car would sit for 48-72 hours at the apartment for what was known as a "decontamination period." If the vehicle remained unmolested, was not towed by the police or was not being watched by narcs or the FEDs, then the vehicle was clean and had made the journey undetected. Police by nature are inclined to action and prefer not to sit and watch a car that may or may not have drugs inside of it for three days. If a car had not been touched or watched after 72 hours, it was safe. After the decontamination period, Desean would return to get the vehicle to take it to a garage where it was opened and the narcotics were removed.

Red's Mexican sources in Arizona used a large RV with hidden compartments which was driven by a married couple to pick up the proceeds from the sale of Red's drugs.

The cash was counted and assembled in banded stacks. The stacks of currency were sealed tightly in clear plastic using a food saver vacuum sealer. Sometimes a layer of scented dryer sheets was wrapped around the currency before they were vacuum sealed in a measure to reduce detectable drug odors.

Once a bag of money was handed to the couriers working for the drug sources, that specific drug debt was cleared from Red's books. If the couriers were stopped in transit to Arizona and had lost the money load, it was not attributed to Red. It was a loss that was taken by the drug suppliers. Conversely, if money was lost or stolen before being turned over to the couriers, then the money was still owed by Red and had to be repaid.

It had taken Pancho almost a full week of surveillance to find the cab driver. His name was Noel and he worked for a company on Truman Road east of Paseo Boulevard. Noel was a frequent drug customer of a dealer named Ramon who Pancho was hired to track down and eliminate. Noel was nothing more than an unwitting trail of breadcrumbs to find Ramon's location.

Noel was not difficult to spot. He was a very large man who wore unusually thick glasses with large frames to support the lenses. Noel had fashioned a string necklace around his neck to which he fastened the carrying clip of his cell phone. He was too large of a man to be able to fish his phone from his pockets as he drove and found that this method suited him. It resembled a necklace with a large pendent but in the place of the jewelry was his phone.

Pancho followed Noel as he began his shift each day, leaving the cab garage at 10:30 in the morning. Noel usually picked up fares in midtown as far south as 63rd Street but once in a while he was dispatched to the city airport. His daily predictable routine proved to be his downfall in his contact with Pancho. Noel was lazy even by standards of a small Kansas City cab company. He was always in the pursuit of a beverage or small meal between fares and would never clear for service until he was adequately refreshed between runs.

Noel ate at the same restaurant every single day, stopping only at the Town Topic Hamburgers at 2021 Broadway. He had made an arrangement with a waitress or cook to bring his meals out to his cab parked curbside so he would not be burdened with having to exit his vehicle and enter the establishment. Noel would take his sack of burgers to a parking lot where he would sit with the windows down listening to jazz or a baseball game. It was not uncommon for Noel to steal a brief nap around this time as well.

On the sixth day of surveillance, Pancho left his vehicle a block from Noel's cab which had just parked for lunch on Southwest Boulevard near Washington Street. Pancho walked along the sidewalk until he reached the rear passenger side door of Noel's cab entering the vehicle, which was unlocked.

Noel quickly addressed the intrusion between bites of his burger, "Sorry man, I'm out of service right now."

Pancho waited for enough time to pass before speaking to ensure that the encounter was more significant than just a fare, "You on another lunch break?"

Noel's eyes strained through his dirty smudged glasses adjusting the rear view mirror to see Pancho's face, "Hey man, I didn't know it was you. Shit! How are you doing man? I, I didn't know you were back. I thought you was in Iraq killing all them fucking terrorists." Noel's pleasantries were unsuccessful in hiding his concerns. It was evident Pancho had purposely sought him out and had waited until he was accessible.

Pancho kept his answers direct so there would be no misunderstanding in the ensuing conversation, "I need to visit a friend of yours. His name is Ramon."

Noel paused as if needing more time to recall this name from memory, "Ah, I don't think I know any cat by that name. Where does he live brother? I can take you there if you've got an address."

Pancho looked out of the window before responding, "He's a tall thin man, wears his hair in braids and drives a black Marauder with rims. I need you to take me to his spot."

"Uh, well, okay. Has he done something? Is there a problem? I can call him if there's something we can talk about," Noel put his thick greasy fingers on his chest as he began to reach for his cell phone.

"No, don't call him. Just take me to his spot," Pancho instructed firmly.

Noel calmly responded, "He's at 24th and Elmwood."

As Noel put the car in drive, Pancho instructed Noel to not make any stops or call anyone during the drive. Noel had heard Pancho use the term of "spot" which was reference to a location dope was sold from. Ramon was a doper and not much of anything else. Noel assumed Pancho's reason for visiting Ramon was drug related in nature.

Noel and Pancho arrived twenty minutes later and drove through a litter strewn, brick paved ally parking behind a two story multi unit building. The building was very old and had the original bricks from its construction in the early 1900s. A wooden staircase climbed the back wall of the structure leading to several low income rental units. There were signs some of the units were occupied by families. Ramon's Mercury Marauder was parked near the building.

Pancho questioned Noel, "How many guys are inside?"

"Usually two or three. Hey Pancho, if you're going to rob this cat, he might be light today. Shit, why don't I find out when he's holding and then I'll give you a call. We'll come back," Noel suggested.

Pancho interrupted Noel's attempt to circumvent the situation and directed Noel to find a way to get him inside.

Noel sheepishly asked, "How do I do that?"

"It's a drug house, tell him I want to buy some drugs," Pancho aggressively responded.

Noel stopped talking and adjusted his glasses. He was done with trying to stall and divert Pancho. He knew Pancho was much more of a dangerous person than Ramon and quickly decided his fate lie with compliance of Pancho's plan, whatever it would be.

Noel exited the cab with painful difficulty. His atrophied legs strained under the weight of his enormous body. He lumbered towards the bottom of the staircase but surprisingly, he was able to ascend the staircase reaching the second floor. Pancho allowed Noel to catch a few breaths before nodding to him that he was ready to knock on the door.

Noel heard a voice behind the door after knocking the door, "Yeah."

"It's your boy. It's me!" Noel loudly spoke through the closed door.

Ramon could be heard moving something behind the door that sounded like a wooden cross beam which probably securing the door from being kicked in. The door cracked open and Ramon's eyes winced from the sudden bright light of the outdoors entering the dark room he was standing in.

Noel politely asked, "Hey brother, you got time for me and my man today?" Ramon adjusted his gaze and eyed Pancho. Pancho's eyes were concealed behind sunglasses and he remained quiet waiting for permission to enter.

Ramon returned his focus to Noel, "Yeah, why didn't you call first brother?"

"Sorry man, my phone died. My man's in a hurry. You got a couple bigs you can break off?" Noel asked.

Ramon gestured for the guests to enter, "Yeah, let me check. Come in."

Noel and Pancho cautiously entered a dimly lit kitchen. Ramon was tall, maybe six foot two and was built with a thin lanky frame. Another man was sitting at a round table in the center of the kitchen. He was a bald black man with a thin goatee. He glanced up quickly while sealing the paper of a joint using his lips to moisten the edges of the paper. The man kept to his business and began to shuffle a few small dime bags of marijuana scattered on the table.

Ramon and Noel engaged in brief small talk before moving straight to business. Noel vouched for Pancho and asked for two ounces of cocaine. Noel knew Ramon only sold half and full ounces of powder cocaine and crack. Noel hoped Pancho was aware of this and had the money to cover the cost of the order.

As a veteran dealer on the streets, Ramon had survived to the ancient "street-age" of 32 by learning to read people and their intentions with striking acuity. Ramon felt uneasy looking at Pancho. He was too clean and stiff. He was definitely not polite as he had not said one word of a greeting since entering the room.

Pancho noticed a pistol gripped shotgun which was partially concealed behind the refrigerator. Ramon could also sense Pancho was scanning the room carefully. Despite his trust of Noel, he could sense something was not right. Ramon kept his distance from Pancho and positioned his body closer to the shotgun.

Ramon spoke, "I got a couple O's for you. It's all loose and not hard. Is that okay with your boy?"

Pancho did not take this window of opportunity to ease the tension in the room by affirming the details of the product offered by Ramon. He steadfastly remained silent forcing Noel to speak on his behalf, "Yeah, that's cool."

Ramon turned his head and yelled into the next room, "Lonnie, bring two bigs up for me!" Ramon was not a particularly smart individual but he was the Stephen Hawking of sizing people up he did not know. Pancho wore a thin leather jacket which was probably uncomfortably warm for the weather outside. Ramon could also see enough printing through the clothing that Pancho was wearing a pistol at his side under the coat, most likely in a holster. Carrying a weapon was not a deal breaker and was usually expected. However, most of the guys on the street who Ramon had dealt with rarely carried a firearm in a holster on their strong side. It was usually tucked into the front of their waistband or held in the small of the back or in some other casual manner. A lot of guys carried a piece small enough to fit in a pants or jacket pocket. The weapon being carried by Pancho in this position in a holster was an oddity for this situation, in Ramon's experience. For a lack of better wording, it wasn't "ghetto enough."

Ramon attempted brief conversation with Pancho again hoping his fears would be diminished with any response from the silent man. The unnerving silence continued again which even forced the man at the table to notice something was not right in the room.

Noel spoke again for Pancho but had difficulty in keeping his voice from trembling as he spoke, "Hey man, he's not here for a job interview, we're just here to get some work and then we got to be going."

It was now decided. Ramon had been robbed on many prior occasions and had been shot five times during his career. He knew this was nothing more than a simple old fashioned crack house robbery about to occur. Ramon quickly lunged for the shotgun. Pancho swept his coat aside and produced the handgun from his waistband holster with amazing rehearsed speed. Pancho knew it would take Ramon a couple of seconds to retrieve the shotgun and get it into a fire-able position. Pancho placed a single shot into the man at the table who was trying to stand and pull a silver revolver from his waistband. The man was hit in the center mass of his chest and fell backwards over his chair. The second and third shots of Pancho's weapon were so close together that it sounded more like one loud shot. Ramon was hit in the neck and the side of his rib cage. Ramon fell to the floor and the shotgun bounced out of his hand with a loud clatter on the tile floor.

The room was filled with heavy smoke from Pancho's pistol. Noel let out a gasp and instinctively ran for the door as if he possibly had the ability to escape if he could move quick enough. Effortlessly and calmly, Pancho fired two shots into Noel's back causing him to fall to the floor in a spectacular crash. Noel rolled onto his side screaming and pleading for Pancho to stop. It was evident the shots had not penetrated any vital organs. Noel's large glasses clung to his face but had fallen around his mouth. He looked toddler-like in his struggle and screaming. The phone on his necklace had broken loose as well. Pancho stepped forward at an angle in order to execute a head shot over Noel's contorted body which successfully entered the center of his forehead.

A young black kid ran into the room who was probably eleven or twelve. His eyes were wide with disbelief at the three bodies now laying on the floor. He held out his outstretched shaking hand holding a plastic bag of cocaine he had retrieved at the request of Ramon. He slowly let the bag fall to the table as if the drugs still needed to be delivered for purchase.

Pancho holstered his weapon out of sight under his coat and asked the child, "Are you Lonnie?" Lonnie could not speak and simply nodded in affirmation. Pancho carefully looked around the floor and retrieved the six spent shell casings which had been ejected from his pistol during the shooting. He had counted each of his shots and retrieved the exact number of casings that had been spent. He removed the taxi keys from Noel's pocket and dragged his large body from blocking the door. Pancho ran his hand over his short cropped hair as if it for some reason it had been disturbed or tussled during the violent affair and he wanted to compose himself before leaving.

CHAPTER 4 - THE KC STREET NARCOTICS UNIT

Shale called a Monday morning meeting at 9:30 a.m. at the cave for the narcs. He stood towards the front of the room and was dressed in pleated pants and a collared shirt. He appeared in business casual attire but for the cave, he might as well have been dressed in a tuxedo with tails, cane and a top hat. The guys knew if Shale had put on the collared shirt then you needed to be on time to the meeting and paying attention.

It was my first day of reporting to the unit and I was still shocked that I had actually made it. It felt weird not to wear a uniform. I was simply in jeans and a t-shirt. I looked around the room which looked like the audience of a Lynyrd Skynyrd concert or the waiting area inside of the Department of Motor Vehicles office in Toledo, Ohio. Minus the women, everyone had decent facial hair and was wearing concert t-shirts. Most of the guys had work boots on, even the guys who were wearing shorts.

Shale always criticized the narcs for spending too much time on their appearance. He said he could always tell a narc because they had a "clean-dirty" appearance. He described this as a normally groomed person who tried to appear from the streets by simply wearing their hair longer, growing a well trimmed beard or by their clothing attire. They weren't really dirty but just looked like they tried to be. In fairness, he was right. If you saw a person on the street, they didn't trim their goatees for 20 minutes in the mirror. They didn't put product in their hair. They slept in their clothes for a week straight.

Shale had other testimonials of wisdom which he shared from time to time about attire. The only one I found useful was his advice on shoes. He believed you could tell a lot about a person based on their shoes. He said during foot chases people sometimes took off their shirts or made other changes to their appearance to confuse pursuing officers but a person was not be able to change their shoes. It was a great identification tool for the streets. He advised when buying dope to notice the suspect's shoes in the event that person had to be identified later from a group of people and you weren't absolutely certain of their facial identity.

Shale began speaking when the room was assembled and settled, "To those of you I haven't formerly met, welcome to the Street Narcotics Unit or SNU for short. My name is Sergeant Ryan Shale. With our three new arrivals to the squad, we are staffed with nine undercover detectives. You'll be assisted by SNU TAC, which is an eight man tactical raid unit which exclusively executes only our search warrants.

This is a difficult unit to get in, as you already know. This is the most excitement you will experience in your law enforcement career, bar none. On the other side of the coin, this is probably the most dangerous job there is other than a deep sea oil rig worker or a pizza delivery guy in Detroit.

For our new detectives here today, you will be trained by a senior detective who has done this before, knows what works and what doesn't. Please follow their instructions closely. I'm not looking for long term, deep "Serpico" win the drug war investigations. You're all street junkies, dusters, crack heads and "BEMS." You will be making low level buys of crack, weed, meth and heroin. You'll make the undercover buys to get the warrants for nuisance drug houses and then our SNU TAC squad will execute your warrants. Is everybody tracking me?"

"What's a BEM, sarge?" asked Country.

"Its a booger eating moron," replied Shale. The room forced a small chuckle at Shale's acronym joke. Shale paused for a moment in the event his joke had not been digested fully and more laughter was still forthcoming.

Shale walked to a cabinet and retrieved his skull, "Here she is folks, Señorita Calavera. All the tips are prepared by Alice on these papers. You'll pick one at random with your fellow detectives when it's your turn to do so." Shale demonstrated removing a piece of paper from the skull, opening it and reading it to the group, "All right, for example, 1326 Lawndale. Coke and weed being sold with lots of foot traffic and prostitutes at all hours of the day. Ask for Carlos. No further information. From this point, you roll out with your undercover buy money, knock on the door, ask for Carlos, get inside with your great undercover skills and buy some coke or weed. We write the search warrant from your under-cover buy and hit the door two days later. The department gets a gold star for closing another nuisance house. Tuesdays and Thursdays are for outdoor corner buys. Is everyone still tracking me?"

A nervous female detective Marlene, tried to ask a question in a shaking voice without being called on to do so, "Um, but what if I go to a house drug house and um, I go in, and then I see that there's some drugs and um, then I know that—"

Shale glanced at his watch before interrupting her, "Listen, if you have questions, concerns, comments, insults please get with your senior training detective. Thank you everyone. Also, good news, the brass has green lighted $200 more a week for buys. Each of you can now spend up to $500 a week. No more excuses for not being able to meet quotas. All right, get on the streets. You can't buy dope sitting at your desk."

The detectives got up from their desks and picked up their backpacks before leaving the cave. Each narc carried a back pack containing their supplies for the streets. They contained envelopes of pre-recorded buy money, police issued radios, small drug testing kits, notebooks and some even kept their firearms in their backpacks and not on their person. They collectively exited the office to scatter across the city in search of their next targets and new houses.

It was busy at Red's barbecue restaurant throughout the day. There were steady regulars for lunch but the larger crowds usually came in between five and seven in the evening. Red came to the restaurant four or five days a week and spent his time in the kitchen or his office. He had a staff of employees including an experienced kitchen manager who knew how to cook decent barbecue and manage a busy kitchen staff of six to eight people.

Red felt relaxed at the restaurant and took pride that the people working for him weren't criminals and relied upon his "expertise" and leadership for a paycheck. He flattered himself as an entrepreneurial businessman of the people who was a stern yet fair boss to work for.

Red was notified by his cashier someone was in the dining room and had asked to speak with him by name. Red already knew who was coming to see him and quickly went out to warmly greet Pancho and escort him back into his office. Red and Pancho closed the door to the office which was mildly cluttered but comfortably furnished. Red sat in his worn captain's chair before speaking, "I heard everything went great."

Pancho seated himself on the couch and responded without trying to sound overly concerned, "That kid, Lonnie. We're not going to have any problems with him later? He saw a lot of stuff, including me."

Red sat up in his chair and quickly assured Pancho that Lonnie was a beloved close relative and was trustworthy above all other associates he knew. Pancho dismissed the concern as quickly as he had brought it up for discussion, "Well, he sounds like a good person and I'm not worried then."

Red enjoyed explaining his reasons for deciding the fate of people around him even if his audience did not want to receive the information. 'Pancho, one of my houses got knocked and they grabbed up two whole ones. Ramon told me he wasn't there at the time so everything seemed cool. I asked one of the Super Friends to take a look. My man confirmed Ramon was there and got himself snitched up for the FEDs. These young bucks, Pancho, it's hard to find good people these days. But you're not here to listen to my problems or eat my barbecue. Let's get your bag."

Pancho, who wanted to appear empathetic to Red's difficult business decisions responded, "Well, it's none of my business Red. You did what was needed to be done."

"Well, I feel better justifying why I have to make these difficult decisions from time to time and sometimes I feel bad, Pancho." Red paused in an exaggerated gesture before finishing his sentence, "But only sometimes." Red let out his usual high pitched laugh which provoked a rare chuckle from Pancho.

Red located a thick envelope of cash in his desk which he quickly turned over to Pancho for killing Ramon. Pancho placed the envelope in his interior coat pocket and was deliberate to not count it in front of Red.

Pancho spoke before standing, "I'm guessing the Super Friends are cops? How does that relationship work?"

Red was excited to share his exploits of dealing with crooked cops, "Well, the Super Friends, they're super-expensive. We help them from time to time and in return they leave our people alone. As long as not too many junkies get killed in our spots, especially the white ones, we get a free pass. It's like a symbee.., uh a symbee.."

Pancho politely helped finish Red's thoughts for him, "A symbiotic relationship."

Red clapped his hands together, "Yes! Exactly! Thank you. Say Pancho, been thinking, I could use a heavy hand like yours at some of my spots. It pays good and you'd just have to babysit from time to time, keep fingers from getting sticky, stuff like that."

Pancho stood and prepared to leave the office, "Sorry Red, I don't know the dope game. Don't really care to learn it, either."

Red was appreciative of Pancho's honesty in declining the offer but knew Pancho was still his greatest asset for the heavy lifting that had to be done from time to time, "Hey that's cool too, brother. Just glad you helping me out with what you do best. Hey Pancho, how long you been in the army anyway? You kill that Bin Laden mother fucker yet?"

Pancho gave a slight smile before leaving, "Let me know if anything comes up, Red. I'll be around."

There were no hard and set rules at SNU. There was only the legacy of advice that worked for the others before you. If you saw a guy who had been in SNU for two years and he wasn't a slug and made decent cases, you copied everything he did and said with slight tweaks to your own preference. I followed Country with my backpack as we left the office headed to the garage where we would find my undercover vehicle.

Country and I walked through an underground parking garage attached to the cave. It was large enough to hold all of the narc's undercover cars and the two tactical raid vans which were used for the four to five drug raids conducted each week. We walked past an odd assortment of old junked cars in different states of disrepair. What the SNU narcs lacked in their undercover hairstyles and clothing attire, they made up for their choices of vehicles. They were all seized vehicles from drug arrests and DUI's. Most of the narc cars were vehicles that could not be sold at the police auction. If a car was unable to be sold at a police auction where cars are almost given away for free, it was donated to the police academy for some practical driving exercise or donated to SNU.

I found my vehicle, a black 1996 Jeep Laredo at the end of the garage parked against the wall. All four tires were completely flat and the battery had long been dead. The windows were so dirty I could not see the interior of the vehicle. The doors were unlocked so I took the initiative to check the interior as if this might impress Country for some unknown reason. The car smelled musty and every part of the vehicle's upholstery was filthy and marked with cigarette burns. I was told Scott Skinner had once used the Laredo for a week which immediately increased its blue book value to "legendary" for me.

Country looked at the vehicle, without trying to laugh, "All right brother, here's your slick whip for the streets, a beautiful Jeep Laredo."

I responded, "You sure it's not too flashy? I guess if you throw in the undercoating package and a cassette player, I'll take it." Country laughed loudly and helped me get it towed to the police garage where we got it operational.

Country and I made another stop which still stands out in my memory more than others do. We visited police headquarters and met with an old timer named Randy who ran the police armory and other equipment programs for officers and detectives. Randy was thin and walked with a cane. He had been a police officer in days long past but was medically retired after being shot on duty in the late 1980s. He was a good guy who put the officer's safety and comfort above all other priorities. If the officers were being issued recycled damaged holsters, he didn't have a problem with walking into the chief's office and demanding the problem be fixed immediately. He pissed off the management with his demands but at the end of the day, if Randy needed something for the ranks, it got ordered, period. He had an entire basement floor under police headquarters for himself and his staff of two full-time assistants. It resembled some odd underground James Bond bunker training facility.

We arrived to Randy's shop and waited at the counter. Randy appeared with a smile and yelled, "Roderick Superfly Clay! Is this the baby narc you were mentioning?" Randy sized me up and I'm sure he was less than impressed.

I respectfully jested back, "Its that obvious I'm the NFG in the room?"

Randy responded, "Welcome to the club, I was standing where you were back in 89."

Country's timing was no less than perfect, "So Randy, what was it like buying illegal tobacco from the Indians?"

My childish belly laugh was interrupted by Randy, "Don't listen to that clown, you'll have a lot of fun. First some old guy narc advice, always carry cigarettes."

"Okay, but I'm not really much of a smoker Randy."

Randy advised, "They're not for you. You give em' out to people on the street. Great way to make friends quick, and buying dope is all about making friends. All right, let's get you started kid." Randy began to place pieces of equipment on the counter and read the name aloud as each piece was placed before me, "One, baby Glock 27, two magazines with 40 caliber ammunition. One ankle holster for the baby Glock. One undercover State of Missouri driver's license under the name Dewey Davis."

I was taken back and thought it was an inside joke with Country, "Who was sniffing glue when they picked that name?"

Randy continued the list as if he had not heard my displeasure with my new undercover name, "And the most important piece of undercover issued equipment, one cellular Nokia rat phone." The phone was a second generation cell phone and was bright banana yellow. It felt odd in my hand. I examined it but it seemed unimportant.

Randy disagreed with my assessment, "Make sure this is always charged. This is your lifeline. This will save your ass. Did you hear what I just said, Dewey?"

The smile evaporated from my face as I looked down at the phone again, "Yes sir, always charged." We exchanged handshakes and I thanked Randy for his advice which would later save my life. There, however was one small follow up issue before we parted ways, "Hey Randy, any chance I can get a new undercover name, I really like Martin Riggs?"

He turned his back to me as he slowly retrieved his cane to head towards the interior offices of the James Bond bunker, "No sir, it's Dewey! Be safe out there guys."

CHAPTER 5 - BECOMING DEWEY

I visited a few uniform shops until I found the perfect top. I had a patch with the name "Dewey" sewn to the front of my new uniform shirt. Underneath I wore the standard wife beater tank top undershirt. For the bottom, I found plain blue work pants to finish the ensemble. The shoes, of course, were work boots.

The narcs all had back stories and avatar personas to follow like the script of an actor. You needed to know your undercover name better than your real name. If you were making small talk inside of a house talking about work, you needed to have some knowledge of the job you purported to do in the event someone with the same job was in the house with you. For me that was the easy part. From working in a printing press factory for years, I was surrounded by co-workers of all sorts. There were some who had lost fingers coming into work stoned and trying to operate some machine that exerted thousands of pounds of pressure per square inch. I worked with a guy whose wedding ring actually saved his finger from getting snipped off like a piece of string. The machine whined to a halt as his ring squeezed tightly around his finger. I had decided I was now Dewey Davis, the printing press technician who worked a night shift across the state line in downtown Lenexa, Kansas.

I met Country early at the cave to get my undercover buy-money checked out from Alice. After receiving your money, you xeroxed copies of the serial numbers in the event your buy money was found later in a dope house during a drug raid. You never made markings on the bills as seen in the movies. I always thought it was funny how people looked for secret markings on each bill to tell if it was undercover buy money. I imagined myself drawing glasses on each face of the presidents on my government issued bills before buying crack with the money.

I was excited but my nerves were getting to me. I had always been a person filled to the brim with anxiety. When I went through periods of intense anxiety, I would lose my appetite. It was difficult to eat until some of the stress came down. This endeavor was out of my comfort zone. The thought of becoming someone else was so foreign. All the powerful authority I had possessed in uniform was gone with the blink of an eye. I was no longer an experienced and respected officer at East Patrol with a badge, ticket book and the ability to arrest a person. I was now just this junky moron with the worst name possible. Would I get my ass kicked on the street for no other reason than my name being so stupid? I found out later Shale picked people's undercover names. He didn't have the nerve to give you a tip sheet without hiding behind the skull but he took pleasure from handing you your undercover name to deal with.

I was always a little too vain. I took pleasure in keeping a nice expensive hair cut and clean shave. At six foot four, I was on the edge of being a little to thin for my height but it never really showed through all of the gear I wore on my uniform.

In four months I would lose over 25 pounds of weight from the anxiety filled, appetite reducing journey of entering four to five drug houses a week. Loss of sleep from violent occurring nightmares hitched a ride alongside the reduced appetite journey. I would also develop a healthy smoking habit that far eclipsed the cigarette smoking career of my mother in law. My eventual flourishing mane of an untamed neck beard, unhealthy weight loss and a filthy uniform that clung to my bony frame would soon erase all vanity that I had possessed.

Towards the end of my SNU journey, I made people uneasy in grocery stores and restaurants with my appearance. I had difficulty looking at myself in mirrors at home. How's that for undercover work, Scott Skinner? I would successfully transform myself into one of the interesting people I met on calls each day, or found lying in the streets or shuffling around all night like a zombie looking to score.

Country and I hit he streets. I jumped in his car and he took me to a great fishing spot to get started and get my feet wet. We stopped the car against the curb near 39th Street and East Amour Boulevard. I asked Country how much a crack rock costs and began to fish through my envelope to retrieve whatever denomination he suggested. The average crack rock costs eight to ten dollars on any inner city street corner. Someone who is a new face in the area may need extra incentive to get a dealer to part ways with a rock. Usually a crisp twenty dollar bill can help smooth the transition. If someone looks like an undercover cop on their first day, a twenty is definitely required to make the deal happen.

"When in doubt, lure them in with greed, Dewey" Country advised. I put a fresh twenty in my work shirt pocket behind my pack of smokes. "Dewey, see the older guy on the bicycle over there? That's Camo and he's always got crack. He's an easy target."

I acknowledged his location with as much confidence as I could portray. "Yeah, old homey over there on the bicycle. Perfect, do you want me to go over there now?"

Country laughed, "Fuck Dewey, he's not coming to the car, get your ass over there."

I exited the whip and began making my way towards Camo who was sitting on his bicycle which was on the sidewalk. He was looking around the area for any familiar faces. He was an old "smoker" around 60 missing most of his teeth who frequented the midtown corners on his bicycle selling rocks to whoever wanted one without much care of the results. In the world of narcs, Camo was as low as you can get on the tree of street corner dealers. He was the training wheels for baby narcs learning to buy dope. My heart was racing. He might as well have been Chapo Guzman holding a rifle with scorpion designs decoratively etched into the stock of the gun. There was no turning back as I made my way to his corner.

I greeted him with, "Hey dog, you cool?"

He smiled, "What's up, big man?"

It was now time to go deep undercover, "You got the hook up for a 20?" I flashed a small corner of the bill in my pocket so Camo could see I was a real player.

"I'm sorry officer, I'm not sure what you mean," he replied.

I was not discouraged and brushed it off, "That's funny dog, seriously can you help me out?"

His smile got even bigger, "You sure you're not five-o?"

I responded without hesitation, "I'm straight dog if you are."

He looked in different directions up and down the street as if looking for my back up team sitting in a surveillance van, "Let me see your money." I pulled the bill out of my pocket and held it in my hand. He spit a small piece of crack cocaine wrapped in a clear plastic bag from his mouth into his hand. The little baggy was sealed with a tiny knot at the top of the bag. He handed me the crack and I quickly passed him my Andrew Jackson so there would not be any fear of a dangerous drug rip ensuing. I quickly pocketed my saliva covered treasure and returned to the undercover ride. As we pulled away from the curb, I didn't see Camo as he had immediately left the area after the sale.

I prematurely celebrated my victory, "Oh, what's this Country? Felony narcotics packaged for distribution and sold to an undercover police officer, a class A felony my friend. You're welcome, Kansas City, for me cleaning up this corner."

Country looked down at the baggie, "Let me see that, Dewey. Yeah, that's gank brother."

I was unfamiliar with this term, "What's gank? Is that a new drug on the streets?"

He laughed so hard I think he had trouble driving the car straight,

"Gank, it's bunk, soap, fake dope. Its imitation crack. You just got stone cold ganked, Dewey." I was defeated. Country looked over at me sitting in dismay, "Lets try somewhere else, little buddy, I got some good spots where you can buy some more soap."

We hit a dozen more street corners that day. Each one was an embarrassing failure in front of Country, Shale and the other narcs. After each encounter and attempted drug purchase, we packed up and moved to another street corner. We broadcast our locations over the radio to our back up car occupied by two SNU tactical officers who waited a block away.

The tactical officers enjoyed failure from the narcs. They thought undercover work was a useless endeavor. It didn't hold the weight of smashing down doors with a battering ram and clearing dangerous houses. They weren't bad guys but I really didn't socialize much with them. They loved their job immensely. If they weren't training then they were lifting weights. If they weren't lifting weights they were training. To their credit, they were big guys who worked hard at doing their job and kept the narcs safer on the streets.

As I returned to the car after depleting most of my buy money purchasing pieces of soap, I heard the radio from the TAC guys, "Hey Dewey, let me know if I need to turn my shirt inside out and help you out." The TAC guys always wore black t-shirts with police insignia printed in large letters. I guess the joke was they could hide the letters on their shirts by turning them inside out and then jump out of their police car to buy some dope.

Country did his best to be positive, "Forget those clowns. We can do their jobs. Anyone can kick down doors. This is an art. Takes time to learn this." I was appreciative of his patience.

My failures, I imagined, were similar to an actor on a stage forgetting his lines on opening night before a full house. You were basically performing in front of other people each time you walked up to a corner dealer. There were always ten other cops on the list at any given time who wanted your spot at SNU if you couldn't pass muster. Shale made the calls on who stayed and who left his squad. Who knows how long he would tolerate me throwing the squad's buy money into the air with no results. My anger grew as I could not understand how a drug addict with half a brain cell could pull this off where I couldn't. The first week was very humbling and much more difficult than I had imagined.

I mentally blocked the first week from my mind and came back with a better mindset and vowed to not give up, hoping Shale would not kick me out of the unit before I had a chance to improve. I called Skinner on the phone and introduced myself in an attempt to solicit his advice. I think he was already aware of who I was and how things were going for me. He told me he had struggled in the beginning which I found hard to believe. Maybe he was being empathetic.

He kept it short, "Don't try too hard. Buying dope is about making friends. Be friendly but don't be a pushover or weak. Imagine you're buying something that's not illegal. You're just buying a cigarette or a bag of weed." He also mentioned something that I would eventually hear from Tammy, "Don't show fear. Crack-heads don't get scared. They'll get run over by a car, get shot in the leg and still get up and look for dope." The call was over and I remained awake throughout most of the night dissecting his advice.

I grabbed a new envelope of buy money from Alice and asked Country if I could ride alone in my Laredo to help focus a bit on my own. He was not offended and understood my request. I mentally put on a "don't give a fuck" attitude. I took off my shirt and walked around the streets bare chested smoking a cigarette with a beer in my hand and my hat turned backwards. During this time, the department allowed you to carry a "prop beer" with you while doing undercover work. I abused this rule to some extent. I did my best to resemble the great military war veteran Mike Taylor with his wine box. The light had turned on in my head and I started making a few buys on my own during the next two weeks. I wasn't getting "ganked" or at least I could spot the people who would try to rip me off. I wasn't setting any records at SNU but I was on a better path than before and at least improving.

Unfortunately, Shale had other plans for my future within his unit and still wasn't impressed with my efforts. Country and I were between buys sitting together in the Laredo when Shale's voice came over the radio, "Hey, Country."

Country picked up the radio to answer, "Yeah boss."

"I want Dewey to try a house call," Shale requested.

I looked at Country with surprise. Maybe Shale was finally giving me some credit for my efforts.

Country cautiously asked over the radio, "You sure we're ready for that boss?"

Shale responded as if irritated by Country second guessing his training suggestion, "I'm sure; 2349 Wabash, meth and weed. They only serve white tweaker looking guys. This might be Dewey's thing."

Country and I rode together in the Laredo to Wabash and didn't talk much until we arrived. We could see a small dirty yellow house with at least a dozen motorcycles parked on the front lawn and knew we were at the right place. We didn't need to even look for the address on the house. It might as well have had a large neon sign that displayed the words "BIKER METH HOUSE."

Buying baggies of dope on street corners is like playing flag football with your friends at school. Buying dope inside of a drug house is an NFL playoff game to the Super Bowl. That's the extremity of comparison between these two events. There is no funny "gank" stories inside of a drug house. You're confined inside of a building with drug addicts and drug dealers. It's as real as it gets and there isn't a do-over reset button or Shale prop shotguns.

Country was apprehensive but remained calm as he gave me more advice, "Listen, you can do this. Remember the rules. No basements under any circumstance. Never tell people you came alone, you always tell people that you got a friend outside waiting on you. You copy me Dewey?"

"Yeah, thanks, Country." I turned on my rat phone and went through a series of prompts on the keypad which turned the phone into a one way listening post for Shale and Country to be able to hear me inside. Shale gave confirmation over the radio that he could hear me through the phone. I slipped the phone into my pocket and threw $100 into my pocket not really knowing how much meth cost.

"Relax, Country. Seriously, what's the worst that can happen in a drug house full of meth fiend outlaw bikers who hate cops? They're probably not going to let me in anyway," I suggested.

Country didn't seem amused by my sense of humor but gave a patronizing chuckle as I left the vehicle and walked towards the house.

I knocked on the roughly worn exterior of the door. I prepared myself for rejection which actually settled my nerves as I knew I would never make it past the threshold of the door. I looked around the squalor of the porch and only imagined the horrors inside.

I tried to leave when a gauntly thin pale woman opened the door for me. I began to greet her with my rehearsed song and dance but she interrupted me, "Come in, they're waiting upstairs." I was thankful we were off to a good start. I was actually inside of the house and wasn't heading into the basement as Country had advised against. Basements were forbidden for narcs to go into. Your rat phone can't be heard in basements and there aren't enough possibilities of quick exits if you needed one.

Shale would always warn the narcs, "Basements are where people go to die."

I ascended the stairs with the woman following closely behind. It was quiet but I could hear voices talking as I reached the top of the stairs. The stairs led to an A-frame attic which had been partially finished. After exiting the stairway, I was standing in a room being used as storage. The floors were dusty and cluttered with motorcycle parts and an assortment of stolen property. At the end of the large empty room was a doorway to another room where I could hear the voices coming from.

The woman continued to follow me until we arrived to the next room which was considerably smaller. I slowly entered with my hands placed casually at my sides in plain view as to cause the least possible amount of concern from my unexpected intrusion. As I entered the room it was crowded with at least ten people sitting on the floor. It was mostly men but there were two women in the room including the woman who had followed me. There was a blanket on the floor in the center of the room and a few milk crates turned over being used as makeshift chairs. Most of the men had matching jackets which I could tell were linking their association through a motorcycle club. They were all white but one of the women appeared Hispanic.

I picked a spot to sit down that wasn't too uncomfortably close or far away from anyone else. The woman who led me into the room closed the door behind us. She locked the door using three or four security slide bolt locks. The door was hollow set against an old wooden frame which didn't stand much of a chance against a battering ram or even a boot. However, I knew if I had to leave the room through this door as an escape, I would not be able to get the locks open quickly. It was not a viable exit in an emergency.

We were taught upon entering a residence, to first scan all of the available exit points and keep them to memory. While looking for exit points in a room it was also a good idea to look for any weapons lying around or on a person. Some narcs thought it was a good idea to mention the observation of a weapon through casual conversation so that your back up team could hear on the rat phone that there was a weapon in the room with you. Shale discouraged this which was a point I agreed with him on. He said it was better not to talk about a weapon that was simply lying somewhere in the event that a person's attention was now drawn to it since you had mentioned it. There was not a good reason to point out a handgun under the couch so that someone could pull it out and start playing with it while they were smoking dope.

The only exit I saw was the window. I was lucky as there was a pitched roof line under the window that was over the porch. If I needed to jump out of the window I would fall a couple of feet onto the porch roof instead of falling ten to fifteen feet to the ground. I could then hang and drop from the porch roof to the front yard.

I immediately spotted the guy who was running the house or at least the room. He was kneeling and looking out of the window. He was in a good vantage point where he could see traffic in front of the house on the street for a fair distance in both directions. He had long straight hair scattered across his shoulders and poorly drawn tattoos on his arms. He was wearing jeans but was shirtless. He was thin and muscled as if he had done some work-out time in prison recently. He glanced at me as I sat down but didn't appear surprised at my arrival.

He focused his sights intently on something outside, "You see that mother fucker just sitting out there in that jeep? Who the fuck is that?"

I knew he was looking at Country and this would be a great time to introduce myself to the party, "That's my boy. He's just waiting on me. I'm Dewey. Don't worry, I just told him I stopped by to say hi to my girl." I winked at the thin woman who wasn't even really listening to our conversation anyway. "I got money for a ball if you can help me out, brother."

He affirmed my request which was another good sign, "Yeah that's cool, we got you Dewey. My guy will be here in a minute." I knew from his response the dope was not there, inside of the house and was being brought by a dealer, hopefully already en route. I glanced around and saw two people smoking from glass pipes. The people in the room didn't look like the "sharing" type so I probably didn't have to worry about someone asking me to smoke while I was there.

The nervous biker looked out of the window again, "You see that big van down way the street? You guys seen that van on the street before?"

I had no idea if he was looking at Shale's van or some other van. He gave it a few more minutes of his attention before sitting down. The room seemed quiet now. I remembered hearing casual conversation before I had entered and now it was a vacuum of silence save for a few cigarette lighters clicking on and off. I knew my arrival had chilled the room.

The person sitting closest to me was a large guy with a neck beard much more impressive than my own. He was wearing a sleeveless vest and holding a massively large plastic drinking mug. I had seen people filling these mugs at QuikTrip gas stations with what seemed like a full liter of soda. I always laughed when I saw people drinking from these reservoirs.

I knew that was my cue to throw out some pre meth-purchase levity, "Hey brother, that's the biggest mother fucking mug I've ever seen. I guess you got a drinking problem, huh?"

It worked as he let out an unexpected laugh, "Fuck yeah, you can hold six beers in this thing."

I was on a roll and kept it going, "Shit dog, give me a call when that's filled up with a couple pints of muthah-fuckin' bumpy face." The crowd was warming up as I heard a few chuckles.

In retrospect to this day, I should have just shut the fuck up and waited on the dope to arrive. Now that I was funny "meth-head" Dewey the entertainer, it was rude not to offer Dewey a small hospitable puff from your meth pipe. A hand in the crowd quickly passed me the pipe.

"No thanks, brother, I'm riding my bike tonight and I can't get pulled over faded. I'm on probation already. Know what I mean?" I cautioned my biker associates.

The large biker paused between gulps from his mug, "I thought you're with the guy outside in the Jeep."

I would need to tap dance a little bit at this point, "Yeah, well, I am, but he's taking me back to my bike. It's back at the shop. But anyway how long your boy gonna' be? I'm in a hurry, dog."

The guy at the window curiously asked, "What kind of bike you got?"

My mind raced. I knew motorcycles were really loud and had two wheels instead of four but that was the limits of my knowledge, "My bike? Um, shit, brother, it's a Kawasaki 500, I think, with a V8, dual chrome exhausts. Got some cool ass fucking leather saddlebags and a bitch seat for, the bitches."

He waited for me to finish making up a motorcycle out of thin air before asking, "How many CC's does it got?'

He might as well have asked me to solve one of those math problems involving two trains leaving separate locations and to calculate their meeting time. I threw out a number which seemed a safe guess, "Uh, hm, that's a good question, probably at least a hundred." He slowly rubbed his beard and the room was again silent.

The Hispanic female spoke up, "Your motorcycle got a seatbelt too?" Her question came off really bitchy as she was definitely the mean girl of the meth biker lunch table. The room felt really hot to me now even though there had been a comfortable cool breeze coming through the window the entire time. There were no more smiles and no one chuckled. The biker at the window started to reach his hand out of my view towards the small of his back while asking, "So, how did you say you knew about this place, Dewey?" He would not make eye contact with me and I could tell his question was nothing more than a stalling technique until he had retrieved whatever was behind his back.

Country had trouble hearing the audio of the rat phone feed. Shale spoke over the radio, "We lost the ear, Country. We're going to tighten up our spot. There might be a problem in there."

There was no need. I was already out of the house. I had borrowed my buddy's massive QuikTrip mug and knocked it against the hollow head of the rude house guest on the way out the window. I wish I could have smacked the mean biker bitch on the way out the window too. I dropped from the roof and ran towards the Laredo. I jumped in as beer bottles were thrown from the window at our car. Country extended his hand and middle finger out of the window towards the house as we sped away. I hadn't seen him that excited as he was screaming and cursing at the bikers.

I was more worried about Country's critique of what had happened inside the biker house than from anyone else. I was surprised and relieved as Country was actually impressed of how I had handled myself and was thankful a full blown extraction did not need to be called in.

When it came to house buys, the narcs established two outside lifelines, "distractions" and "extractions." The first was always the preferred lifeline and was simply another narc arriving to the scene of the first narc having difficulty and assisting by providing a distraction.

Years prior to my arrival, a female undercover was in a house struggling on a buy. There were two guys inside who were complete assholes. The realities of life on the streets is that female drug addicts often pay for drugs through sex trafficking. The female narc was being pressured to provide a sexual encounter to the two dealers inside of the house before they would allow her to leave. A second narc providing a distraction knocked on the door to the house yelling loudly and pretending to be her jealous husband looking for her as he had passed by the house and saw her car parked in front. He yelled and threatened to call the cops or kick the door down himself to retrieve her. It worked immediately and she was allowed to leave without incident.

The other lifeline is used only in a life or death situation. It almost always resulted in the SNU tactical squad shooting someone inside of the house. It really didn't need much explaining and pretty much occurred as most would think it would. A narc who was being assaulted would have to cling to life until the calvary came and smashed down the door. When this happened all rules were thrown out of the window. If you were a bad guy inside of the house during an extraction it was an extremely bad day for that person. If you were just an uninvolved junky by-stander inside the house during an extraction, it was also an extremely bad day for that person.

Country assured me that the biker house was one of the more difficult houses he had seen in a long time and didn't think it was fair that I had been thrown in there without more experience. Country was careful not to go much further in his criticism of Shale and kept our conversation on a lighter note, rather than tarnish Shale's decision.

Country said that some of the best narcs in SNU had been involved with extractions even at no fault of their own. "Dewey, we've done extractions for informants and we've even done extractions for other people in houses who we didn't know. They were just being beaten to death and we had to prevent them from being killed. I mean, they're dope houses, Dewey. Only bad shit happens inside of those places. That's the cost of doing business."

The homicide detectives could tell stories for hours of crews kicking doors of dope houses in and laying down gunfire while stealing as much dope and money they could find. There had been dope houses with everyone in the house being marched into the basement and executed during robberies.

Country, however did provide more advice to always keep in mind. "Dewey, always try to stay away from larger crowds if possible. The less people the better. It only takes one guy to run his mouth which will get the others going, saying that you're a snitch or a cop."

I asked Country, "Tell me the truth, if someone put a gun to you and told you to smoke dope, what would you do?"

Country laughed, "Hell yes I'd smoke that pipe like a champion crackhead, Dewey!"

We both laughed but he assured me I would survive having to smoke a crack pipe if it ever came down to that situation.

We stopped on our way home at a small hole in the wall to decompress with a couple beers before calling it a night. It was an Irish pub which was always quiet and you had to be let in with the click of an electric door unlock switch operated by the bartender. A closed circuit TV was used to get a view of anyone who wanted to come inside just to keep the place a little safer.

I asked Country if there was ever problems with police corruption. He said it was funny I had asked him that and asked me if I knew a guy named Curt Lessing. I was better with remembering faces than names and was having trouble recalling that name.

"He was a tall blonde guy who usually drove one of the wagons at Central Patrol," described Country.

"Wait, I think I know him. He kind of looked like a surfer guy and talked real loud?" I asked.

"Exactly, that guy!" exclaimed Country.

I remembered him. Lessing had been sent as my second car on one of my calls during my probationary period. He was actually a really nice guy who helped me through the call instead of sitting back and watching me struggle. He always talked a slight decibel louder than what was necessary. Maybe he had hearing loss or something.

Country told me he was fired two weeks ago when he got wrapped up on a minor drug possession charge. It started with a guy who was arrested in Metro patrol with a half pound of marijuana and a gun under his car seat. He immediately squealed like a pig, saying said he could give up his neighbor who was a cop and bought weed from him. The guys at SNU and Internal Affairs were called in to interview the guy. It turned out to be true that Lessing bought an ounce of weed every once in a while for personal use from his neighbor, nothing more. It was unfortunate but it was against the rules and he lost his job.

A lot of cops who get involved in illegal activities don't understand that they provide the greatest "get out of jail free" card of all time with whomever they're involved with. When it comes to a dirty cop, everyone wants to be a part of the process of taking him down, prosecutors, judges, the FBI, the DEA, State Police, Internal Affairs and the list goes on. It's always open season on a dirty cop.

CHAPTER 6 - INFORMANT 3071

Shale called a roll call meeting to hand out tip sheets or at least let the skull hand them out. Starting from the back of the room, he walked around the room with the jar letting each detective pull a tip sheet from it.

"We left off with Ernie on the last round" Shale reminded the narcs. Ernie was a detective of Dominican origin. His hair was jet black which he wore slicked to the back of his head and he had a small goatee. His comedic timing was always impeccable.

He drew his sheet from the skull while announcing to the room, "Just don't give me a Dewey house, boss, I don't want to get my ass thrown out a damn window."

Another narc, Anson, joined in, "Hey Dewey, motorcycles don't come with seat-belts."

Anson was a large black man who was more naturally stocky than muscled. He had been at SNU longer than anyone else in the room with four years under his belt.

I knew this was coming and was probably deserved. I sat and waited for the laughter to dissipate regarding my meth house spectacle. I sat and hoped the embarrassment would dissipate quickly.

Shale remained focused and refused to acknowledge the laughter in the room or comment on what had happened at the house. He approached Country who was sitting at the desk next to me, "There's an in-custody arrest who wants to work off her charges. Have Dewey do her paperwork. He needs to run an informant till he learns how to buy dope on his own."

As Shale pulled a paper from an envelope, Netta turned around from the desk in front of me and giggled, "It's okay, Dewey, I don't know about bikes either. Maybe next time you just talk about stuff you know about, like Star Wars monsters and stuff."

I genuinely laughed at Netta's comment. I liked Netta a lot. She always seemed independent from the crowd of the other people around her. She wasn't really a follower, which I liked. She was half Mexican, had short spiky black hair and was fluent in Spanish.

Shale stood before me with a piece of paper he was reading from, "Tamera Josephine Mack, female, 38 years of age. Arrests include; possession of cocaine, sale of a controlled substance, stolen auto, assault, domestic assault, public intoxication, indecent exposure, forgery, retail theft, burglary, drinking in public, urinating in public, resisting arrest, passing bad checks and trespassing. Good luck with your new informant."

I picked up her rap sheet and thanked Shale, "Thank you, sir."

Shale walked to the front of the room and announced, "We need to knock down eight more houses this week to make quota. Let's get out on the streets. You can't buy dope sitting at your desks."

Almost all drug cases, whether at the local municipal, state and federal level, rely upon information received from human sources. These human sources can be utilized to assist law enforcement in obtaining evidence needed to prosecute drug violators.

In the majority of drug cases, there isn't a "victim." It's considered a victim-less crime. The government takes the place of the victim which allows a charged defendant to offer proactive assistance as an informant to the government. An informant is often a defendant in a drug case who is seeking to proactively assist the government (the police) for anticipated reduction in their sentencing. Sometimes informants are just people who want to work for money or other personal reasons and are not under any judicial obligation.

Tammy fell into the category of an informant working off drug charges. A week prior, Tammy met up with her friend and long time associate from the streets who was known by the nickname, Tweety Bird, or simply Tweety.

Tweety was visually the opposite of Tammy, being taller, much darker in skin color and thin. She had been on the streets much longer than Tammy. She was a regular drug user and had been using crack daily for at least 8 years. Tammy did her best to look out for her friend who seemed to invite problems wherever she traveled. Tweety refused to ignore or concede to people who disrespected, slighted or diminished her, instead choosing to escalate the encounter into a verbally loud and sometimes physical disturbance which usually summoned a dispatched patrol car. Despite Tweety's thin frame, she loved to fight people when she was inebriated and high. She had grown up in a violent home and it was now built into her nature that this was a normal manner of behavior when you were upset. Tweety was never strong enough to defend herself physically when provoking others so she was a frequent guest at the emergency room at Truman Center Hospital.

Truman Center was located in downtown Kansas City, Missouri and was the default trauma emergency room for the majority of people involved in shootings, stabbings and car crashes. The best trauma surgeons in the city staffed the emergency room at all times. On the weekends, it was filled to capacity with the wildest of people.

Tweety was built for stamina as she would smoke and remain awake for two or three days at a time especially when she was using heavily. She would voyage throughout the city at night visiting a multitude of hospitable drug houses until she became belligerent and was asked to leave. Strangely enough, it was actually possible to be kicked out of a crack house for your behavior if it disrupted drug sales to other customers. Tweety had been blessed as she had not yet been found beaten to death after a bad night with the wrong people. She had been shot twice, stabbed a few times and even run over once with a car but she persevered with her adventures. She loved to party with Tammy who looked after her and protected her when she was vulnerable and making bad decisions.

Tammy and Tweety were together early into the evening at an apartment on Prospect Avenue south of 20th Street. The apartment unit was located inside of a small red bricked building that housed four separate units, of which only two were occupied. A white man named Tom in his late 60's lived on the second floor in the North unit of the building and would permit addicts, drug pushers and prostitutes to use his apartment for social gatherings as long as he was present and could share in the vices of the festivities.

Three years later Tom was murdered in his kitchen by a man he had never met before who had randomly drifted through Kansas City after being paroled out of Smith State Prison in Glennville, Georgia. After bludgeoning Tom to death, the parolee innocuously sat on the front porch of the apartment until dispatched officers arrived and arrested him without any sort of resistance. He took a plea for the crime without offering any account or reason for his actions.

Tammy, Tweety and five additional guests were gathered in the living room with Tom. Tom always occupied a worn and filthy level handle recliner which was respectively off limits for any guest to sit in even if Tom was not present. The room was dimly lit with two table lamps. The ceilings and walls were discolored from years of smoke stains. The carpet was an unusual pattern of earth tones which helped camouflage the years of filth trapped in the fibers. There were filled ash trays and empty liquor bottles scattered throughout the room and set aside in corners. Heavy un-circulating smoke constantly filled the air of the apartment. The windows were covered with sheets of opaque plastic or newspapers to shield from view the illegal activities of the occupants inside. There were no curtains which gave the interior an even more unsettling appearance to anyone who wasn't a regular patron at Tom's.

The only pleasant item in Tom's apartment was a nicely framed painting of the SS Edmund Fitzgerald, a large Great Lakes freighter which sank in Lake Superior during a storm in 1975. The image showed the ship struggling on a night-time voyage against rough white-capping waves. People often stared glassy-eyed at the painting as their minds received chemical infusions from pipes or needles.

Tweety loved to dance and wiggle her small frame when she heard music. She wasn't partial to any particular type of music but loved to fall into the rhythmic patterns of the sounds with her movements. She would appear to be in a trance when she danced as she always kept her eyes closed and tried to mouth the words of the songs. Tom would often play music from an old Sony stereo in an attempt to lure Tweety to the dance floor and get the party more festive. As was the case on this evening, Tweety was in the center of the room dancing alone.

Tammy was smoking a cherry flavored Black and Mild cigar watching her friend move about dance floor. Tammy chuckled at Tweety's contorting movements and yelled, "Shake that lil' tiny white girl ass, Tweety. Make it clap a little bit."

Tweety's eyes eerily opened widely as she quickly challenged Tammy back, "I guess you think you can do better, bitch?"

The patrons in the room became excited at the challenge and yelled over the music for Tammy to move to the dance floor. Tammy accepted the challenge from her friend and began to dance in the center of the room while holding her cigar safely clenched in the corner of her smiling mouth. Tom increased the volume of his stereo to an obnoxious level and started clapping his hands to the music. Tammy purposely brushed her large frame into Tweety knocking her over while she danced causing the room to erupt in loud yelling and more laughter.

Two patrons at the party sat on a couch conducting a discreet drug transaction as the rest of the room enjoyed the Tammy and Tweety show. Netta was purchasing $50 worth of crack from a man inside the house who was known on the street as Pony. He flashed several clear plastic bags of cocaine from his pockets for Netta to look at in an attempt to impress her with his inventory of available product.

Netta handed Pony her pre-recorded SNU buy money and politely thanked him for the sale. Pony asked Netta if he could leave with her to which she declined and said she had to meet a customer who wanted the drugs she had just bought.

Tom glanced unconcerned at Netta as she left the apartment and continued to clap at Tammy and Tweety dancing.

Several minutes had passed after Netta exited the apartment when the sound of glass breaking was heard over the music. A metallic canister fell through opening of the broken living room window, landing on the floor of the room. The canister spun for a few rotations on the floor before violently exploding with enough concussion to shatter the remaining windows of the apartment. Tammy and Tweety were knocked off of their feet.

The Kansas City, Missouri Police SNU Tactical Raid Team quickly breached the door of Tom's apartment with a battering ram despite the door being completely unlocked and assessable by simply opening the door. The door frame splintered apart as the team poured into the room. In a matter of a few minutes all seven remaining occupants including Tom were cuffed using plastic restraints and sitting on the floor with their legs crossed in compliance with the officers orders.

It was a routine executed almost daily across the city with successfully repeated procedures. The team breached the structure and secured all of occupants inside of the residence. After the residence had been secured, Shale entered with a few detectives in tow who searched for evidence.

Pony was arrested and taken from the scene for sale of a controlled substance to an undercover police officer. The detectives did not find any contraband on Pony's body. When the "flash-bang" initially entered the living room, Pony threw three plastic bags each containing one ounce of crack cocaine from his pockets onto the floor. In an unlucky turn for Tammy, she landed on two of the bags of dope as she fell to the floor. As the officers moved her into a seated position to be handcuffed, she had the drugs underneath her body.

Shale introduced himself to Tammy and attempted to converse with her about the discovered contraband, "The party is over and who are you?"

Tammy winced with displeasure from the pain of the restraints around her wrists while trying to answer Shale, "Tammy."

"Have you been arrested before, Tammy?" asked Shale.

"You mean like today?" she responded.

Shale chuckled at Tammy's humor, "I've seen you around from time to time. Where are you from?"

"I live at 1310 under a fucking rock. These God damn things are too tight. Loosen these!" Tammy demanded.

Shale ignored Tammy's demands and asked her if she knew the people in the house with her. Tammy refused to cooperate with any forthcoming information. Shale held the bags of drugs found underneath Tammy for her to see, "Does this belong to you Ms. Tammy? This looks like crack cocaine."

Tammy roared with anger, "Hey, you just put those there! Those aren't mine you hairy nipple head."

Shale was amused by Tammy's creative profanity but was stern when addressing the seriousness of her situation and informed her that she was now under arrest for possession of a controlled substance. Two East Patrol officers were dispatched to meet Shale at the Prospect apartment to transport Tammy and Pony downtown for booking.

The next day, I had asked one of the guys at the Jackson County Detention Center to move Tammy to a separate holding room where I could talk to her out of earshot of other prisoners. My requested accommodations were provided as I visited Tammy on the women's side of the facility.

When I arrived, I was escorted to a windowless holding cell where Tammy was sitting on a cement bench attached to the cell wall. Her shoes were off and she was stretching her feet looking at her toes as I entered.

I tried to pause my introduction for a bit of dramatic effect as I entered the cell which unfortunately allowed her to speak first, "Damn boy, what they get you for, smuggling sausages down at pickle park?" Her reference was in regard to a public park in midtown where married men came late at night to indulge in gay encounters with younger escorts who worked the area. They were often arrested for misdemeanor indecent exposure charges when the Central Patrol cops in that area were bored and were looking for something to do.

I didn't give Tammy the satisfaction of reacting to her comment, "I'm Detective Jeff Moore with the Kansas City Street Narcotics Unit."

"Sorry, officer. I though you was here for my conjugal visit. You a lil' skinny vanilla bean but, mm-hm, Momma like." I could tell she was still upset over her arrest and wanted to make anyone's life more difficult.

I didn't want to start my proposal to her in an antagonist manner and simply told her, "I'm not here by choice."

She forced a laugh and responded, "Me too!"

I gave her a short sales pitch without too much gloss thrown in to let her know I could have her back on the streets today with a chance to reduce her charges. She tried to argue the dope wasn't hers but I told her it would be difficult to convince a jury or judge of that argument considering her arrest record and being found inside of an active drug house where an undercover narc had just purchased dope. She started to see both sides of the coin and the realities of her situation.

"All right, what do I got to do?" She asked with an odd expression on her face, clenching her mouth tightly.

"Do you know what an informant is, Tammy?"

"You mean a snitch?" She aggressively responded.

I explained that her identity would be concealed from public record and she would only be referenced by a number in any police reports. I mentioned that our unit worked with informants on a daily basis and we had a great record of keeping them safe and influencing the courts with their charges.

She looked at the wall as if she was thinking intently before she spoke, "What I got to do, Detective? You need me to sell dis' on the street?" She pointed at her rear end and laughed loudly, "You gonna' make a lot of arrests. Hope you ready for no more criminals on the streets."

I honestly could not tell if she was being serious at this point or if it was more gamesmanship coupled with her odd sense of humor. I told her, "I need your help to get in dope spots. You point out good houses and people holding bags of dope. We're just buying rocks and bags everyday. That's it."

"I ain't going to court. I ain't test-a-lying," she announced firmly.

I was brutally honest with her and really didn't like what came out of my mouth next, "There's no court for this. Believe me, no one really goes to jail anyway." As I heard myself speak, I had just realized most of our undercover sales cases were quickly pled to probation unless someone had a gun in their pocket when they were arrested or had a very extensive criminal record. It was extremely rare if someone was arrested on probable cause inside of a drug house or apartment during the drug raids. Again, you needed to be caught red handed inside of the house with something on your person. If the room had ten people in it and dope was found in a cabinet or under a couch cushion, you couldn't prove physical possession to support an arrest. We simply took the dope, and hoped this would slow the house down for a while. My honesty surprised her and I think she had some appreciation I was being forthright from the beginning.

She gave me a nod of approval, "All right then, we're gonna be Cagney and Lacy. I'm ready, Detective."

"You can just call me Dewey. I'll finish your paperwork and be back in an hour to get you."

She gave a small wave with her hand as I turned towards the door to leave, "All right Dooby, take your time, I got to knock out a deuce anyway."

I again kept my reactions in check not wanting her to think her vulgar humor was either acceptable or insulting to me at this point. I knew I was under duress to make this relationship work or I would simply be shuffled back to East Patrol to allow a more accommodating cop to fill my spot at SNU. I would let Tammy make all the insults and jokes she wanted to but there was no equivocating, she would need to get me inside dope spots and help me make the buys or she would be charged with a felony drug case.

I don't know the reasons I was never told that Tammy had worked several years before as a drug informant for another drug squad within the department and had even helped the DEA with an investigation. Maybe her files were protected and the two separate drug squads didn't trust each other. Maybe narcs just don't trust each other in general. Maybe there was something deeper that could not be discussed.

Working narcotics is a strange world. It pulls in people you wouldn't normally expect to be involved in being dirty; city officials, cops, firefighters, lawyers, business people and everyday taxpaying citizens with families. The greed is too strong for some people to turn away from. Hopefully Tammy could show me more of the picture than Country could. She had been in thousands of drug houses and had known as many dealers. Surely she had wisdom she could impart to me.

I led Tammy out of the jail. All of her personal belongings were returned to her which basically was the clothing she was wearing when she had first arrived. I slowed my pace to hers as I had a longer stride than her shorter legs. We walked a full block and found where I had left the Jeep. She sat in the front passenger seat and surprisingly was unsurprised of the dirty conditions of the interior.

She looked around as if taking a mental inventory, "You got any Black and Milds, Dumpy?"

I reached for my courtesy "friend" cigarettes that I gave to people on the street per Randy's advice, "Actually, its Dewey and I've got cigarettes." She declined my offer as we pulled from the curb and began driving north on Locust Street approaching 12th Street.

She saw a QuikTrip gas station and began to point with her finger, "I need my cigars, they need to be cherry Black and Milds. They got em' at he QuikTrip store there. Stop, Dooby. Stop there!"

I pulled into the front lot of the store parking close to the building.

QuikTrip's are great stores. They're clean and if you were in uniform on your shift, you could grab a soda for free. They encouraged it and would not accept your money no matter how much you insisted. The business appreciated the cops coming in as much as possible. I guess it was one of those symbiotic relationships as there was rarely a robbery or other disturbances at their stores.

A local fast food restaurant tried this endeavor in the mornings giving free breakfast to cops in uniform. An entire traffic unit decided to hold their daily roll call meetings there for a large delicious 12 man breakfast every day before starting their shift. Eventually the manager apologized but revoked the complimentary continental cop breakfast. I had even seen a couple of the 15% guys who would wear their uniforms on their days off to try and get a free meal at some of the fast food places that gave free meals to cops in uniform. Regardless, I was no longer a cop in uniform and would not be given anything gratis from anyone.

I handed twenty dollars to Tammy and asked her to bring back change. She entered the store and returned to the Jeep with an armful of supplies to include boxes of her cigars, a large can of beer and she was adorned with a new pair of sunglasses atop her head. It was obvious she had depleted all of the money I had given her. She wasted no time in igniting a fresh cigar which filled our car with obnoxious cherry flavored cigar smoke.

"You got my change?" I asked even though I knew the answer.

"No change, Darby, I needed shades too."

It wasn't even worth picking a battle with her on something trivial like this. I was ready to get moving on a list of houses I had received from Alice. You were required to draw sheets from the skull when it was your turn to do so but it was perfectly acceptable to ask Alice for more tip sheets or even find houses on your own. It didn't matter as long as you were making the quotas of getting warrants for as many doors as possible.

I looked in the rear view mirror to check if I could back the Jeep out of my parking spot when I heard Tammy yelling out of the passenger side window. She obnoxiously rapped her clenched hand on the outside of the door to get someone's attention, "Hey Tweety B! Tweety Bird, What up, girl?" Tweety was standing near a pay phone on the sidewalk in front of the store. She seemed excited to see Tammy and immediately approached the Jeep but oddly stood at my window instead of Tammy's, probably wanting to check me out since I was a new face.

"Big T, what up, girl? I thought you were still in county. What's up with yourself?" asked Tweety.

Tammy expelled smoke into my personal space as she talked across me to her friend, "Shit, girl my favorite two words, no bed space."

I corrected her, "That's actually three words, Tammy."

Tweety noticed me speaking and saw the cigarette pack in my shirt pocket, "You got a smoke, honey?"

"Doofy, give my girl a square." Tammy barked between cigar drags. I quickly removed a cigarette from my pack and handed it to Tweety.

Tweety was appreciative of the smoke, "I'm Tweety. How are you doing, sexy?"

I took the opportunity to make my introduction to her since I doubted Tammy had the manners to introduce us, "I'm Dewey, I'm good, thanks. Where's the action tonight, Tweety?"

She looked over her shoulder before answering me, "Stay off 'the avenue,' the cops are messing with everyone up there. There's a good spot near 11th and Prospect. See ya girl. Nice to meet you, Dewey."

I looked at Tammy smugly, "She got my name right, Tammy." Tammy ignored my comment as I proceeded to pull tip sheets from my pocket.

The avenue mentioned by Tweety was reference to "Independence Avenue," a long stretch of road that ran from Broadway Boulevard in downtown Kansas City to the Blue River just west of Interstate 435. The avenue was a hot spot for outdoor drug sales and had the city's highest levels of prostitution with as many as twenty women working at any given time. It was a part of the city that was safer for addicts and drunks to spend their time milling around. A lot of dealers came from other parts of the city to sell to the people who frequented Independence Avenue. The police were receiving pressure from neighborhood citizen groups to clean up the increasing numbers of addicts, prostitutes and drunks who were spilling from the Avenue into adjacent neighborhoods.

I looked through the addresses, "Hey Tammy, let's go ahead and start on these houses. There's five or six good ones here. We probably need to get our story straight of how we know each other." She seemed confused and asked me to clarify what I was talking about. "If we're asked how we know each other, we should have something ready to say." I explained to her.

She was now drinking from her can of beer and casually suggested, "Yeah, we'll just tell people we're fucking." Her suggestion was not followed by any smile or smirk whatsoever. Again, was this one of her games or was she sharing advice with me to help me get in the houses?

I suggested instead, "Um, yeah, that's okay, but how about instead, we met through a common friend who we know from the bus stop and-"

She interjected before I had finished, "That's stupid, I don't go to no bus stops."

I explained that it didn't have to be a bus stop. We were simply fabricating a story and we could substitute any detail with another.

She took a large gulp from her beer, "I think it's just better if you just tell people you're eating my ass, Dooley."

I scolded her immediately telling her that was the foulest thing I had ever heard a woman say. She was now grinning and trying not to laugh. I decided I would just utilize creative improvisation when we arrived to each house instead of pretending to be Tammy's lover.

We arrived in the area of 11th Street in Bales. I pointed the house out to Tammy that was listed on our sheet. It gave a few details of the types of people who visited the house and notated that drug customers always knocked on the North facing door of the building for entry. I opened a few buttons of my outer work shirt so my tank top was more visible. I prepared the rat phone and had my back up car in the area so I was ready. "How do I look, Tammy?"

She gave me a sideways glance, "Mm, you look like a guy who got fired from his job at a dirty bookstore cause they caught you looking under the stalls watching people slap sausage."

"Really Tammy, what does that type of person even look like?" I legitimately asked, curious of her response.

"Wait, Dundee, I changed my mind, you more like a skinny old weird bus driver who sniffs the seats after people get off the bus." She replied, trying to keep from giggling.

I was losing patience with her and was eager to start getting into houses on my own. We left the Jeep and made our way to the door indicated on the tip sheet. A heavy set Hispanic man looked through the window of the door and simply asked us what we wanted, refusing to open the door. I greeted him and tried to make some small talk but it was difficult to communicate with a closed door between us.

After a few minutes, he simply said, "I don't know you, man, you're at the wrong house."

We returned to the Jeep and moved to the next house on the list. At the next house, the occupant at least opened the door for us but was as coldly receptive as the prior gentleman. We continued moving through the different addresses on our tip sheets moving to different parts of the city making our way as far south as 73rd Terrace.

I felt stiff and too rehearsed as if I was trying to present a sales pitch for selling a product like a vacuum cleaner and Tammy was my assistant who would help set up our product display. I didn't feel as relaxed or fluid as I needed to be. I wasn't "trying to make friends" as everyone had advised me to do.

On the sixth stop of the day, I made it into a house at 46th and Cleveland Avenue and was able to buy a bag of weed from a white woman named "Liz." It was as anticlimactic as any drug buy could be. We sat in her living room while she pulled a plastic Tupperware container from under the couch with a dozen bags half ounce bags prepared. I only remember her now because she told me she was selling weed to help pay for her daughter's wedding which was a few weeks away. I wasn't really proud of this buy and had rather it not really happened but I wasn't in a position where I could throw away a stat. If I had actually been a drug user, Liz would probably be my go-to dealer as she gave a fair price for the marijuana and the weight was accurate for what I paid for.

At the bottom levels of buying dope, you will almost always purchase a bag of dope, then go home and weigh it to find to find that it's short of what you paid for. The price of dope is quantitated by weight and quality and nothing else. You always expect that your bag will get you high but you also hope you got what you paid for in terms of the quantity, which was rare.

The crowned prince of shorting dope and ripping people off was a dealer at East Patrol named Ferron Petty. For years Ferron sold dope in an area between Lexington and 9th Street which covered most of Independence Avenue. He was notorious for ripping off his customers, even the ones he liked. He had no guilt whatsoever in shorting people's bags, selling bad dope, or simply just taking someone's money with nothing given in return. He was a constant problem and for some reason would not go away no matter how many times he was arrested.

In 2002, a construction worker from Raytown, Missouri had lost every dime to his name from a massive crack habit. His wife had long since left him and he was close to "lending" his car away for drugs. That's usually one of the final stages of becoming a full blown junky. You "lend" your car for drugs to a dealer to use and then you try to report it stolen later in an attempt to get it back. It never worked and we would call it a "crack rental." Some guys even borrowed their parent's cars and gave them away for dope.

The construction guy was down to his last $300 dollars and had the misfortune to cross paths with Ferron, who of course sold him $300 worth of bad dope. The man returned under the guise of purchasing another bag from Ferron. Unfortunately, Ferron, who never kept accurate records of who he ripped off, had gotten high and then forgot this particular customer.

Ferron's body was found north of the Avenue on Montgall Street in the early morning hours. The disgruntled customer had fired every round of a fully loaded pistol into Ferron's body. It was sad and unfortunate that the power of drugs led the man to lose his family, his livelihood, his mind and freedom from incarceration but the community was thankful of his service in removing Ferron from the streets.

I decided to pack it in for the day after the weed house on 46th Street. The day was not going as planned. I was too tired at this point to digest what wasn't working and wanted to drop Tammy off at her home without discussing the failures of the day. I let her know that we were done for the day, "These tips are bunk, I think we got bad info on these houses."

She condescendingly replied, "Uh-huh."

I could immediately feel my blood pressure increase and my face became flushed, "What does "uh-huh" mean? It's obvious there's bad information and these aren't good houses."

"You couldn't buy a joint at a Bob Marley concert in Jamaica Dumby," she replied while rudely delivering a wafting cloud of cigar smoke for me to enjoy.

I lost my temper with her, "It's Dewey dammit, not Dooby, Doofy, Dorky, Debbie, Dusty or Dumpy! Just fucking Dewey!" She gave me an evil side eye glance from her side of the car and I realized I had let her unravel my composure. "Fuck! I'm sorry, Tammy. This shit is hard and I can't mess this up anymore."

She didn't seem surprised I had lost my temper nor concerned she had caused my outburst. "Why?" she asked.

"Why, what?" I asked.

"What happens if you mess up?" she asked again.

I explained to her, "They'll send me back to the road and I'll be a wash out. It's embarrassing."

"So this is just about you not being embarrassed? Why do you want to be a cop, Dewey? Why you out here? You think this is a TV show?" she asked.

She had actually used my horrible undercover name correctly for the first time. I tried to give her a textbook answer of how I was going to help people and make an impact in the community but I could not convince her or even myself of my sincerity as I spoke the words. I thought it would be better to just default to our original agreement than turn our conversation into my personal vanity speech.

I reminded her she needed to show me the ropes and that's why I was going to help her with her drug charges. I was honest with her and put away my pride admitting that I was a mistake or two from being kicked out of the unit. I told her if I left SNU, I didn't know if Shale would reassign her to another detective. Country was leaving in two weeks and most of the other narcs had their own informants. I honestly told her that I didn't know what her future would be if I was kicked out of SNU.

She felt sorry for me in a weird way and I think she was flattered someone needed her help. She helped Tweety out once in a while but she had not had anyone in her life recently who genuinely needed her assistance. She knew I was in her world and I would have to play by her rules and games. She was such a strange person to me at the time and I really hoped she would help me out.

She flicked her ashes out of the window for the first time instead of on the floor of the Jeep, "So now I'm the teacher, Dewey?"

"I can't believe I'm going to say this, but yes, you're kind of my teacher," I responded.

She smiled, "Okay, then you're my student but you're gonna have to stay after class tonight real late and work on some extra credit with professor Tammy. I need you to help bang out my chalk erasers. They real dusty. Know what I mean?" She disgustingly wiggled her tongue out of her mouth before letting to a large deep belly laugh.

"Can you be serious for five goddam minutes? Just tell me what the fuck I'm doing wrong," I replied frustrated and tired.

"All right, Dewey, I'm going to help you just because I feel sorry for you. You're like a special kid eating the crayons and licking the windows but I'm gonna try."

" Great. Lay some knowledge on me," I replied.

"Okay, first show me your horn," Tammy requested.

I was confused, "My horn?"

"That's what I said sausage tits. Your horn Dewey, let me see it!" she demanded.

I reached down and honked the horn of the jeep, "Like that? There's my horn."

"A horn is a pipe you nipple head!" she disappointedly admonished.

She would have her hands full. I did not even know the street lingo for a junky's most prized possession, his damn crack pipe. She deserved not only to have her drug charges cleared but to be financially reimbursed for having to educate a moron like myself.

Crack pipes or horns were everywhere. They were sold in inner city gas stations near the cash register. They were sold as clear glass, 3 inch long pipes with a small plastic rose inserted inside of the pipe. I guess the rose made the product look less like a crack pipe for sale. Conveniently, the same store would sell small copper scrubbing mesh pads near the pipes.

To create a crack pipe, you needed to insert a small piece of a copper scrubbing mesh pad into one of the openings of the pipe. The piece of crack cocaine would adhere to the mesh while you held your lighter under the pipe and inhaled the fumes.

It absolutely infuriated me that these stores could legitimately sell the dissembled pieces of a crack pipe with all of their other products. My mind could not make sense of this in any way.

If the smokers couldn't afford to buy or find the glass pipes, they would simply snap a car antenna off and use that equally as well to smoke crack from.

The day was over and it was time to take Tammy home. She assured me tomorrow would be a better day as she had a surprise for me. I tried to prevent my mind from even remotely imagining what it could be and simply focused on driving Tammy to an apartment complex where she was living.

When we first began working together, it felt intrusive to ask her personal questions about her situation, her family or her background. I knew she had a rough life and she was now more or less forced to work with me for lack of options. It was better that I didn't make her feel more uncomfortable with questions while she was assigned to train me.

We would eventually need to find things to "small talk" about to fill the empty time when we drove around for 8 hours each day looking for drug houses. We couldn't be more different than oil and water. What the hell would we discuss; the weather, politics, advances in police sciences? Maybe she would just make jokes all day and mispronounce my name. She literally found a new way to screw up the name "Dewey" each day. It was actually phonetically impressive to be able to create that many variations of my name.

We arrived at her apartment. I never left the Jeep or went to the door when I picked her up for work or dropped her off. I had no idea who she lived with and really didn't want to know. There was always the same older black gentleman at Tammy's apartment who greeted her as she exited the Jeep and walked inside. He was friendly and would wave at me as well.

Tammy would tell me frequently he was her old man but he was totally okay with her fooling around with younger white guys like myself. I would kindly remind Tammy, "We're not fooling around, Tammy, have a good night and I'll be here tomorrow at the same time to pick you up."

CHAPTER 7 - THE TUTELAGE OF TAMMY MACK

The day began again for us as I arrived at Tammy's apartment and honked the horn of the Jeep. The same older black gentleman stuck his head outside of the door and yelled, "She's almost ready, she'll be out in a minute."

I mouthed the words "okay" and gave him a thumbs up and hoped he wouldn't come out to ask me who I was or why I picked up Tammy every day. Who really knows what she told this person about us. Maybe it was better if I didn't know or maybe she was playing some kind of mind game where I would be uncomfortable with the mystery of him.

She knocked open the door with an aggressive slap of her hand and seemed to slightly skip from the steps to the sidewalk. I don't know if she was excited to show me the surprise she had mentioned yesterday or was just full of robust energy.

She got into the Jeep and greeted me excitedly, "What up, Dewey boy!"

"Hey Tammy, you ready to clean up the streets?"

She gave a short but loud laugh and asked if we could make our normal stop. It was now our normal routine to stop for supplies before staring our workday. We stopped at the QuikTrip where I gave her money for her cherry flavored Black and Mild cigars and one beer. I had learned my lesson and began interchanging the customary twenty dollar bills she was given for Alexander Hamilton's. This expenditure was from my own pocket and there were limitations to what I could afford to bribe her with everyday. If I bought a "prop beer" later in the evening, then I always purchased two beers so she would have one as well which would be her second for the day. She would have more than enough cigars and beer for our shift but I wasn't buying her sunglasses and snacks anymore.

She seemed more talkative than normal and was telling me a story of how she was making an egg and toast sandwich before I arrived that was similar to how her aunt had made them for her growing up. I reminded myself to not ask her any personal questions of her upbringing but that didn't necessarily mean I couldn't prod her a bit to tell more of her background without really asking her to.

Her thoughts weren't focused and she quickly changed topics several times as we drove around the city before focusing on work and finding a house to start at. The air was cool but comfortable enough to drive with the windows down. The fresh air made the her cigars somewhat more tolerable.

I thought maybe she had forgotten the surprise so I asked her if she had something planned for us today. She clenched her lips together tightly and made a strange face by filling her cheeks with air and somewhat resembled a frog as she thought about "the surprise."

"Oh, yeah, I got a house for you Dewey so you can learn how to buy dope. We got to train your dumb ass son," she giggled.

"All right Tammy, where's this drug house?" I asked.

"Okay, first we're just going to take Indiana down to 37th and I can find it from there. I don't remember the numbers," she replied.

We drove for what seemed like thirty or forty minutes or more. Tammy's memory wasn't as precise as she had believed it would be in finding the house. I was careful to be patient with her and not show any signs of frustration in finding the correct house.

We arrived and parked in the street in front of a one story dark green residence which Tammy assured me was the place. I put the car in park and shut off the engine. Our back up tactical car was in the area but was on another street to the north and out of view.

I waited for a minute to talk to Tammy in private before turning on the rat phone even though it was only Netta who would be listening. Country was off today and Shale didn't always come out on house buys. Maybe it was a sign that he was trusting me more or maybe he didn't really care if I made it out of a house anymore.

Netta drove a maroon colored 1995 Buick Le Sabre with aftermarket wheels or as some people would say "rims." One of the back side windows was broken out and she had decided not to fix it for effect, instead taping plastic in place of the glass. It was the perfect ride. The car looked so good it could practically buy dope without Netta.

The house was unusually clean and didn't appear like the usual "nuisance house" on the block. There was no trash in the yard or disassembled cars in the driveway or three guys without shirts sitting on the porch drinking beer at ten in the morning.

"Anything I need to know about this place, Ms. Tammy?" I asked.

"There's a woman who sells dope in there, mostly crack but sometimes weed, too. She's real cool with everybody and her kids live here so it's not crazy or nothing inside there," Tammy replied.

It immediately bothered me that there would be children inside and I was unhappy at the thought of a kid seeing me trying to buy dope in my Dewey Halloween costume. I felt as if I should call the Missouri Division of Family Services with an anonymous tip of drugs being sold from inside of the house instead of trying to get inside to buy dope. I knew this would discourage Tammy from proactively helping me with anything else in the future if I didn't follow through with her lesson plan for the day. I needed to strangely trust her guidance for the time being.

Tammy advised that it was always better to be indirect when asking for dope. She gave some tips and a few examples of how to ask for drugs without really asking for drugs. She also said it was a good idea to introduce myself by name. When you gave someone your name, you appeared more honest and less deceiving. You were giving your identity to a stranger. It mentally tilted the scales so that the person should in fairness offer something to you in return.

I prepared the rat phone and Netta flashed her headlights from down the street to affirm she could hear me. I took a deep breath as Tammy could hear the sound of me exhale. She lightly put her hand on my shoulder like a mother patting her child before getting on the school bus for the first day to calm my anxiety with her gentle encouragement, "Don't fuck this up, Dewey."

I lightly knocked and was surprised how quickly the woman came to the door. She was average in all aspects of appearance and was possibly a mix of half African American and half Hispanic origin. She had slightly wavy hair that just touched her shoulders.

"Can I help you?" she calmly asked. She had opened the door so as there would be no obstruction between us during the conversation. She was pleasant and had a kind face which only bothered me and inserted small pangs of guilt in my mission.

"Uh, hi, ma'am, my name is Dewey. I don't know if we're in the right place. I came here a couple months ago with a friend but I can't find my buddy anymore. I was looking for the place we came to and this house looks like the right place" I described.

"Who are you looking for? Do you know their name?" She asked.

"Well, this is sort of embarrassing and I'm sorry, but I'll be honest with you. My friend made me wait in the car while he came inside to get something." I admitted with feigned reluctance.

"What did your friend get?" she asked politely.

I knew she was vetting my story and stalling for more time to decide if she would let us in. She was being careful not to turn me away but was still being cautious perhaps maybe more out of safety for her kids inside than from fear of the police.

"I'm sorry ma'am, we're just trying to get something and we didn't mean to bother you. Maybe we're at the wrong house, Tammy," I suggested.

"Wait, you two look okay, maybe I can help you out. Do you have money?" she asked.

I replied, "We have $40."

She stepped to the side and motioned for us to come inside. I could see from the corner of my eye her scanning the street behind us as we entered. There were several chairs in the living room and I sat on a large sofa by the window. Tammy sat on a chair across from me and I was not sure why she just didn't sit next to me on the couch. I could tell Tammy was accurate with her description of children inside of the house as there were toys scattered on the floor.

The woman asked if we could wait a bit while she called "her guy" who lived around the corner. We told her we could wait for him if she didn't mind. She asked us if she could have our money first which we gave her without any hesitation. I knew from her arrangement that she was an addict and would take a small part of our order for herself when it arrived. This was referred to as "taking a bump" which was part of the arrangement and was perfectly accepted as long as it wasn't a Tammy sized bump. The larger the order meant a slightly larger piece of dope that she could keep for herself. I knew $40 would be enticing for her and difficult to turn down. She wouldn't need to leave her house to get a decent piece of dope for helping us out.

I heard a child talking in the back bedroom and I earnestly hoped the child would just remain in their room and not come out. I reassured myself that the woman had probably prepared for this scenario with our drug deal not being interrupted with the presence of an inquisitive kid.

To my correction, a girl around the age of seven or eight walked into the room with a book in her hand. Her hair was only half braided from someone who attentively weaved an elaborate braided pig tail on one side but leaving the other side a bushy mess. She had a shirt on with a cartoon character on the front and was wearing pajama pants. She had socks on that didn't match or maybe that was how they looked in some weird design patterns. She was cute and had bright large brown eyes.

She sat next to me as though she had known me for years and opened her book to examine the pages. She had no concern or fear from my presence which I assumed was due to her mother being close by.

She paused in reading her book to introduce herself, "I'm Abby, who are you?"

I was irritated and uncomfortable with her introduction. If the woman had not already phoned in our order of crack "to go," I would have

simply left the house at this point. I responded to Abby with a brief introduction of myself hoping she would lose interest in my presence and leave,
"I'm Dewey, very nice to meet you, Abby."

"Do you know your multiples Mr. Dewey?"

I looked down and could see she was holding a math book. There
was a piece of paper she had removed from the book that was her homework but was also a bookmark for the page she needed to return to.

"No, Abby, I'm not good at math but I bet you're smart and you
know your tables real good."

She looked down at her book and held the paper in her hand, "Mr.
Dewey, what is eight and five?"

I gave her the answer but I also corrected her to remember to "say
eight times five" instead of "eight and five" when expressing a multiplica-
tion problem.

She politely thanked me but quickly fired another math problem
at me, "Oh. Thank you. Do you know seven and four? I mean seven times
four, Mr. Dewey?"

I gave her the answer but I was becoming visibly upset. I avoided
eye contact with Tammy because if I had seen so much as a smirk on her
face, I would have picked up a blunt object and struck her in front of the
child.

"Thank you, do you know six and ten?" she asked.

I again reminded her of the correct way to express a multiplica-
tion problem and gave her the answer. She laughed and corrected herself.
I could see as she laughed, she was missing a tooth or two from her baby
teeth falling out. My voice was hollow and didn't sound like my voice anymore. It was as if someone else was speaking for me. My hands were covered in sweat and my face was flushed red. I felt anger as I had never felt it
before.

I could hear the arrival of the woman's dealer who entered the side
door of the house walking into the kitchen without knocking. He was a
young black kid, maybe 17 at the oldest. I could see him talking to the
woman but from my vantage point I could only see her hands. She gave
him our money and he handed her a bag before quickly leaving. He was
careful to keep his back to me so that his face wouldn't be seen.

Abby may have asked me twenty more math problems but I
couldn't hear her anymore. My anger had just shut things off for a bit. I
walked into the kitchen to prevent the woman from bringing the dope to
me in front of Abby. Her back was to me and I could see she was opening

the bag to take her bump. She was startled when she turned around and handed me the bag. I didn't make eye contact and didn't thank her. I just took it and walked out of the door. I didn't wait for Tammy and let the door close so she would have to open it herself.

We entered the car and I aggressively pulled away from the curb. Tammy could tell I was upset as I was confident she had planned for this to happen.

She pulled a fresh cigar from the box and lit the end in a celebration of her lesson for the day, "You were right Dewey, you are helping people by being a cop. You're helping them with their homework." She chuckled and took a drag of her cigar. I pulled the car to the curb and parked.

"Why the fuck did you bring me here, Tammy, to piss me off? That was horrible. That was the absolute worst thing I've ever seen."

She was emotionless as she spoke, "You got drugs from a house on your own. That's what you wanted, right?"

I refused her logic, "Don't play games with me Tammy!"

"Oh, you're upset 'cause Abby's momma is a crackhead. Yeah, that was kind of sad" she mocked.

I lost my temper even though I was being educated beyond my expectations with lessons that would stay with me for the rest of my life. "No, Tammy, it's very sad! We just left her in there! We left that beautiful sweet little girl in there and I'm out here with this stupid shit." I looked down at the bag of crack in my hand.

"That's the game. This is where it starts, with little Abbys, little Dominiques, little Billys and little Tammys. Not all of us grew up in Overland Park, Dewey," she replied.

"Don't play that card with me, Tammy," I snapped back at her.

She seemed more serious now and paused as if preparing to deliver the eulogy at a funeral, "Mm-hm. They gonna smash that door down and come running in with guns yelling like they always do on COPS. I hope little Abby won't be scared when they come. Maybe she got a teddy bear she can hold onto when momma gets taken away. Good job, Dewey you closed this dope house down good."

She had taught me her lesson and had shown me a surprise just as she had promised. I aggressively ripped the bag of crack open and threw it out of the window in an exaggerated manner to emphasize my point. I took a deep breath before speaking, then choosing my words carefully, "Nah, I didn't buy shit in there Tammy. It was a dry hole. Please listen to me real carefully, Tammy. You're going to take me to a real spot with real drug fucking dealers today or we're going our separate ways. No more stuff like that again. Do you understand me?"

Her jaws were clenched and her nostrils flared. I was unsure of what she would do next; if she would get out of the car, yell and curse at me or concede to my warning. I was through at SNU if she left and I would rather quit than see another Abby. My point was made and she knew what I was looking for.

I realized at this moment I had left my rat phone on instead of turning it off when getting into the Jeep. Netta had the pleasure of listening to the entire Dewey and Tammy drama theatre. I knew she was cool and would not repeat what she had heard to Shale so it was of some comfort.

I would have to replace the $40 of buy money with my own personal cash to conceal the expenditure on my balance sheet.

Tammy took a drag from her cigar and soberly threw out a new address, "27th and Kensington." I knew this area well as it was located in my former beat area while at East Patrol. I had driven through this area every day patrolling it for three years. I didn't need to get any clarification from Tammy on this house. I knew it would be a real and dangerous place with bad people inside of it. It was too late to apologize and ask Tammy for an easier "starter" house. I had immaturely played my hand and thrown that option out of the window. She was angry at me for dismissing her "lesson plan" for the day and was paying me back with a nightmare of a house and I could feel it coming.

We arrived in silence after an uncomfortable quiet ride without conversation. The rat phone was prepared and we slowly exited the Jeep.

The house was a two story squalid and dilapidated structure. It met every benchmark of a nuisance house and was difficult to look at in the daylight. As usual, every window was opaquely covered up with makeshift sheets of plastic or hanging filthy linens. We approached cautiously and encountered a man siting on the cement railing of the entry stairs leading to the enclosed porch.

The man recognized Tammy but only gave me a quick glance. "Hey Big T, haven't seen you in a minute. How you been?" he asked.

She ignored her rules of indirectly asking for dope by directly asking for dope. "You guys got any work?"

"We got you, go on in," the man instructed. "Be careful, my man is crazy up in there today."

It was par for the course that there was already a red flag thrown out on the first play. We entered the dark enclosure of the porch and then the even darker living room beyond the porch. I entered behind Tammy and closed the front door behind us. I could see the door remained unlocked as I closed it which comforted me that it could be used as the primary point of exit if something went awry inside the house. A window would not be needed for escape.

The room was substantially more depressing than the outside of the house. Among the litter and garbage scattered throughout the house I could spot empty plastic drug baggies, depleted lighters and charred pipes from the sea of addicts who frequented the house. The room was festooned with spider webs and insects which were moving on the walls and furniture. The roaches were slow to react to any movement and simply walked towards the ceiling if somebody came close to them.

The walls and floors seemed to have a slight oily sheen that may have come from years of poor air quality and circulation inside of the building.

The house was furnished and decorated in the style of a much older person who grew up during a different time period. I was sure the house became occupied by squatters or a relative of the original occupant who had most likely passed away. It didn't appear that the home had electricity. Many of the nuisance houses we encountered were simply unoccupied or uninhabitable dwellings that dealers and addicts congregated inside of. Sometimes people would splice into a live electrical line to a neighbor's house to steal electricity for the dope house, especially in the wintertime.

I quickly claimed a chair near a large TV set that was more inviting than the other pieces of available furniture. There were two lifelong career drug addicts already sitting on a couch together smoking. They were indeterminate of an accurate age due to a lifetime of heavy substance abuse. They appeared as two older black men but they could've been in their late forties. There were friendly and not threatening in any manner.

Tammy had now found a chair to sit in and was looking around the room. She made some small talk with the addicts who were happy to chat with her about people they knew in common from the neighborhood.

I heard voices from one of the back rooms of a woman and a man yelling at each other. From the intensity of the yelling I could tell that a physical encounter between them would ensue. The recognizable sound of furniture being knocked over combined with the woman's cries of pain elevated my concern.

The addicts simply pretended they couldn't hear the disturbance. My body tensed and I prepared myself to stand quickly if the need arose.

A woman ran towards us from the dark hallway behind her who we recognized as our friend Tweety even though she had been beaten badly. One of her eyes was freshly swollen and she was bleeding from several cuts on her face.

A shirtless dark skinned black man who was stocky and much shorter than Tweety ran from behind her and savagely kicked her to the ground. Tweety addressed him by the name Durron as she was screaming so it was evident they were already acquaintances.

He began to kick her in a way I knew would eventually be fatal if it continued for any length of time with his shoes making deep impacts into her rib cage.

Tammy quickly barreled into Durron knocking him into a heavy table. She surprised and stunned him with the power of her large frame. He bounced off of the table and fell to the floor, unable to catch his footing from the impact.

He pushed himself up from the floor and looked at both Tweety and Tammy, deciding what his next move would be. I stepped forward and pointed the barrel of the Glock 27 Randy had given me at Durron's forehead.

"Everyone, get the fuck out of here, now!" I yelled. Tammy lifted Tweety to her feet, shouldering the weight of her thin frame as she helped her towards the front door. The addicts quickly left the house as well leaving Durron and I alone.

I escorted Durron into the kitchen and forced him to lean forward over the kitchen sink. He placed his hands onto the counter to support himself from falling over as I kicked his feet apart so he was now unable to stand on his own unless using his arms to hold himself upright. It was nothing more than a normal frisk position of a suspect performed on the street many times before. Durron was significantly off balance making it now difficult for him to turn around without falling.

I kept the gun to the back of his head as I gave him clear instructions, "Where's the dope?"

He fumbled for his words but eventually pointed me towards the cabinet. I opened the cabinet and grabbed a bag that had about two or three grams of crack inside of it. It was sitting on top of a small digital scale.

He genuinely believed I was going to kill him after taking the dope. "Hey man, just chill, man, yes take it, just take that," he pleaded in a high pitched and frightened voice.

I removed $40 from my work shirt pocket and placed the bills on he counter where he could see the money, "That's for the dope. Is that cool?"

He affirmed my payment with extreme gratitude and kept his posiion without moving. He was actually very compliant, which I was thankful for.

Before leaving, I forced him into the basement. He must have heard Shale's advice of basements being final resting places of the murdered as he pleaded for his life walking down the stairs into the darkness. In fairness, the optics of the situation did appear that I was going to kill him in the darkness of the basement.

As he reached the bottom of the stairs, I closed the door and secured it with a sliding bolt lock. I knew he could simply kick or push the door open and break the lock off but I enjoyed the theatrics of sending him into that dark abyss. It mentally healed me from watching his savage beating of Tweety.

I walked outside and could see both Netta and the tactical car on the street moving closer to the house in the event I would ask for an extraction. I gave them a wave indicating I was okay and entered the Jeep with Tammy and Tweety.

I didn't see Durron as we drove away and I felt satisfied inside imaging him fumbling around in the dark bleakness of his own dope house trying to make it to the light of day.

I retrieved my radio in my bag and broadcast to everyone that we were clear of the house and that it was a "good deal." I mentioned to Tammy as we drove away, "I'm going to enjoy our guys crushing that door."

Tammy and I tried to get Tweety to the hospital which was only 5 minutes from where we were at the time. She refused to go and even threatened to jump out of the Jeep while it was moving if she thought we would take her there. We drove to the QuikTrip on Truman Road near the intersection of Winchester Avenue.

We patched her up the best we could as she composed herself somewhat before leaving our company and walking towards the store. It upset me to see her suffer and I wanted to keep her with us and not let her go until I knew she was safe. We both knew she was hungry for her smoke and would soon find another place to go or perhaps even return to Durron.

It took the house with Abby and now seeing Tweety's unquenchable thirst for drugs despite coming so close to death on so many occasions to force me to realize the power of drugs over the human mind. How could we dissuade someone from using when they would put this above their life and the life of their child?

The adrenaline had left my body and I was incredibly relaxed. I sat in the Jeep and tried to focus on the breeze coming through the window to help me relax further. I was in no hurry to leave and felt like it was better to sit for a moment.

Tammy handed me one of he cigars and I thanked her, "You've never given me one of your cigars, Tammy. This is kind of romantic."

"You're still a dumb-ass, Dewey," she replied. It was her way of thanking me for helping her friend, Tweety.

We both knew how close Tweety was to being killed today and it brought the mood down as we knew she would eventually run out of luck, which she eventually did two years later. She was found murdered with two other people; a man and woman inside of a house in the 2900 block of Monroe Avenue. All three individuals had been shot multiple times. A suspect was not arrested or identified and the case remains open.

I smoked for a while and felt I had deserved the right to ask Tammy some questions about her life as payment for my assistance to her friend. "So, how long have you known Tweety?" I asked.

"Six years and that's a long time for knowing someone in the streets, Dewey" she said.

Tammy told me a story or two about some of the adventures she had been on with Tweety and laughed when describing seeing Tweety dancing for the first time closing her eyes and lip syncing the words to a song while her thin bony frame moved to the beat of the music.

I asked Tammy if Tweety had any kids hoping it would allow me to ask the same questions of Tammy. Tammy said no and surprisingly admitted to me that she had a daughter who lived in St. Louis and she had a son who was killed when he was 19. I was more than content with her sharing this much information and felt it better to not ask any more questions unsolicited unless it was merely a follow-up question to any forthcoming information she would volunteer to me first.

As Tammy and I worked together over the coming months, we would laugh and recall stories of adventures and people we met along the way but we never spoke of the house with Durron again. It was quickly forgotten and we did not recall it to our memories.

My relaxation and Tammy's cigar were both coming to an end as I heard Shale's voice on the radio. He asked for myself and Tammy to meet him for a quick chat. We met with him at a parking lot in midtown near 31st Street and Main.

"How's Dewey progressing, Tammy? You pulling your hair out yet with him?" Shale asked with a smile.

Tammy smiled back, "Yeah, he's as dumb as a box of dildos but he's trying to do better each day, boss," she explained and followed up with a belly laugh.

There was some more small talk but I could tell Shale wasn't really engaged in the conversation. He seemed to be more or less just reading us, as if calculating his evaluation of how long Tammy and I would last as a team before imploding into a failed experiment.

"Netta has some reports to knock out, I'll back you guys up. Just let me know over the radio when you got a spot picked out," he advised.

He thew on some sunglasses and pulled a can of chewing tobacco from a pocket. He neatly placed a wadded clump of the tobacco between his gum and cheek while somehow keeping his hands complete clean of any stray falling tobacco pieces. I would rather smoke twenty of Tammy's cherry cigars than put chew in my mouth. It was strange seeing a guy like Shale partake in a habit like that. I guess every man had his vices in life.

We returned to the Jeep as I fished in the center console for a tip sheet to head to. The decision was easy since I only had one sheet left.

I read the sheet which listed an address I was already familiar with. "Damn!" I exclaimed at my luck.

"What's up?" asked Tammy.

"We can't do this one. It's in a mobile home park and I've been to this guy's trailer several times. He's a crazy one armed army veteran who gets into fights with his wife every other day. She usually beats his ass most of the time. I've arrested him three or four times in the last year and he's going to recognize me," I concluded.

"Is the boss going to let us take a pass on this one?" she asked.

As soon as Shale heard my request to pass the tip to another narc in the squad, he immediately denied my request and further challenged me to rise to the occasion putting my undercover skills to the test. He threw in stuff about the fate of the skull and how it was forbidden and bad luck to trade tip sheets between fellow narcs. He even questioned my desire to be in his squad in a final attempt to push me into making the cold call.

"Dewey, I'll be honest. I haven't made up my mind about you yet. I don't know if you have what it takes to be in SNU. I tell you what, you get in that dirty meth trailer and buy some dope, I will definitely put a gold star on your chart. You need to convince me you want to be here and you want to buy dope in my squad," he challenged.

I had only wished the theme song to "Rocky" was playing in the background as I accepted Shale's challenge. Shale now seemed unusually intent on seeing how this venture would unfold and he was genuinely excited to head towards the trailer for my cold call.

No matter what situation arose, Shale always wanted to push it further almost to the point of failure being imminent. I knew even before asking him that he would not have let me taken a pass on the trailer and I was angry at myself for asking anyway.

CHAPTER 8 - ONE ARMED CLYDE

I had some time as we were twenty minutes away from the mobile home park. I took the opportunity to brief Tammy about the location with which I was very familiar with.

"This guy's name is Clyde. He's got a short temper and he makes me look like a rocket scientist. He's a straight up meth head down to his missing teeth and homemade tattoos. His family is pretty strange too. They've got a son who's messed up in the head, more like, dropped as a baby down a well messed up, than naturally messed up. He doesn't talk and he's built like a silver back gorilla."

"So basically we're gong to visit some of your relatives, Dewey?" Tammy asked.

"Exactly, Tammy, it's my family so you need to behave yourself. Speaking of introducing you to my family, let's get our story straight before we get there," I advised.

"You're my baby's daddy. He's an ugly baby, Dewey but we still love him," Tammy suggested.

"No. We can say…"

Tammy interrupted me, "Okay, Dewey, we're just friends with freak-nasty benefits."

I shook my head and just gave up, instead focusing my thoughts on the layout of the trailer as I had remembered it. Shale assured me he would have a couple of cars in the area in case the one armed guy beat my ass with his "one arm."

We arrived and entered the park which was immense in size. It was a community with its unique personality, ecosystem and problems. The management of the mobile home park really didn't care what was going on as long as they were paid their $400 lot fee for each trailer. Most trailer parks had a few rules to keep the place clean and somewhat nicer in appearance but this was not one of those places. The management didn't care if your trailer was missing the skirt or you had the frame of a pick up truck in your front yard minus the engine. A lot of the trailers were falling apart and the roads between the trailers were unpaved.

There were no background checks and some people paid their rent by subletting to multiple people living under one roof. This led to a lot of registered and unregistered sex offenders living in the same area together along with other people who wanted to live in a place where they couldn't be found.

As a patrol cop we were called to this park every day. The department should have constructed a patrol station next door only servicing calls dedicated specifically for this park and nowhere else.

I had been on calls with decaying dead bodies which did not bother me as much as a dispatched call I had made to one of mobile homes there in July of 2000. I was dispatched to contact a man and woman who lived towards the far end of the park furthest away from the entrance.

Each tenant was asked to bring their garbage to the dumpsters at the entrance of the park where it was picked up twice a week by garbage trucks. This couple instead would take their trash and throw it into a large hole in the floor of the Northeast bedroom of their trailer. The trash fell through the hole and collected on the ground beneath their home. They simply closed the door and placed towels at the bottom to of the door to help control the flies and the smell of rotting garbage.

We were called by the neighbors to investigate the smell, which was mistaken for a dead body or several dead bodies. The couple, who were friendly, assured us they had not killed anyone and invited us to enter their room of trash to investigate. The unventilated trash room in the humid Missouri summer heat had created a unique ecosystem of flies and larvae that was truly horrific by comparison to anything else.

As Tammy and I traveled in the Jeep through the park, I didn't need to look for any addresses or street signs as we approached our location. It was exactly the same in appearance as when I had been there a dozen times before. Tammy was quiet for most of the ride through the park and was interested in looking at the scenery.

"This is sad, Dewey. Is this where a lot of you white people live?" she asked with a sheepish grin.

"All right, Tammy, if things go downhill, I'm just going to punch him in his toothless meth face and we'll run out of there," I assured her.

"Damn, Dewey, you're going to hit an elderly disabled one armed military veteran. That's messed up," she admonished.

We parked the Jeep and sat for a minute before getting out. I had already prepared the rat phone before driving into the mobile home park. Our back up tactical unit was unable enter the park without raising some attention to our presence so a few of the narcs were positioned inside of the park instead, as they were able to blend in with the residents undetected as the police.

Shale, Anson and a narc named Paul were my back up team. Paul was a SNU detective who had been in the squad for a year. He had a long blonde beard and resembled a Norwegian Viking to some extent apart from his heavily tattooed arms, which were a full canvas of elaborate tattoo sleeves. He was bald but never allowed you to see his head as he always wore a cap no matter where he went. He never really spoke in front of other people so it was hard to gauge his personality or what his thinking was on any discussed topic in the office.

The inner door to the trailer was open but the outer screen door was closed. I could hear a box fan from inside that had a slight whine to its motor. I casually knocked on the door knowing Clyde was inside since he rarely went anywhere.

He rose from a recliner chair and approached the door. It was difficult to see him through the shadows of his trailer. As he stood in the doorway, I could see he remained unchanged during our absence of seeing each other for several months. His left arm had not grown back and he still refused to wear any type of shirt over his body no matter the occasion, the weather or what time of day it was. He did not have any fresh ink added to his weathered sun damaged skin.

Frequently prison tattoos are created in limited colors of dark green or black similar to Clyde's tattoos but the guys in prison who were the artists usually had some degree of artistic talent. You really didn't see any prison tatts that were as poorly drawn as Clyde's. It was almost if he had drawn them himself using his remaining arm.

I didn't want him to have the opportunity to speak first so I was quick to greet him, "Hey, brother. My name is Dewey and this is my friend Tammy. I'm not sure we're at the right spot. Maybe you could help me."

"You look familiar kid, do I know you?" he asked.

Maybe this was a normal greeting he gave to strangers or maybe he in fact could see some resemblance through my appearance that recalled memories of Officer Moore.

"Uh, I don't know, I'm from Raytown. I used to come up here with my cousin to visit this guy. He lived around here. Shit, Tammy what was that dude's name?" I asked her as part of my ruse.

Before Tammy could answer, Clyde focused his attention to Tammy. "Is that your girlfriend?" he asked without any reservations of possibly offending her with his question.

I knew Tammy would thrive from the reference made by Clyde so I tried to extinguish the possibility of us being a couple before she could respond, "Um, her, no she..."

"He just lets me sit on his face sometimes. We're not serious though. We're looking for lil' Gary. He's a skinny white mother fucker. He look like a noodle with fucked up teeth," she interrupted and answered with a larger smile than I had seen on her face before.

Clyde had been a smoker probably since he was five years old and gave a raspy old smoker's laugh from Tammy's tawdry admissions of our relations. His beard was light brown but it was heavily stained from his daily nicotine intake.

Clyde couldn't remember who the president of the United States was but he seemed to be legitimately trying to recall anyone named Gary from his vacuous foggy memory, "I wish I could help you and Tammy but I don't know this Gary guy with the messed up teeth."

I could tell he was interested in just the pure oddity of the company Tammy and I would provide if we stayed and chatted with him for a while. He wasn't in any hurry to dismiss us and I could tell he was waiting for the opportunity to invite us into to his home.

"Hey, that's cool brother, thanks for your service, though," I said glancing at one of his military tattoos that was of much higher quality than the others.

"What was that?" he asked. I could tell he had heard me and merely wanted his ego lifted by me repeating the compliment.

"Your tattoo there. You're a Nam guy, right?" I asked, clearly seeing him swell with pride.

"That's right, son, 7th Marines, two tours," he announced with clarity.

"My dad served, too. He was a pilot, flew B-52's in the war." This backstory was easy for me as my father had actually flown in the Vietnam War but I cringed at the thought of using his war service to further my connections with Clyde. It seemed disrespectful in a way, I guess.

"Well, well, I knew a couple of those fly boys over there. Hey Dewey, what are you two lost souls looking for? Maybe I can help. Come on in, it's as hot as two rats fucking inside of a wool sock out there. I got some beer inside if you want to cool off," he offered as he gestured for us to enter.

We stepped inside as it was only a few degrees cooler but was equally as humid as the air outside. It was cluttered and crowded with junk Clyde or someone living there had collected. It wasn't as filthy as I had remembered but the air had an odd smell to it as if it wasn't really clean. I could see an old box fan in the window that drew in some fresh air but wasn't powerful enough to really circulate the smell from the trailer.

"Hey, thanks brother, what's your name?" I asked as I found a seat for myself on a couch and let Tammy find her own spot. Tammy decided to sit next to me on the couch and was sitting uncomfortably close to me.

"I'm Clyde. Welcome to my castle, Mr. Dewey and Ms. Tammy," he politely welcomed us.

Clyde's old lady Loretta, a sizable unkempt woman with a few poorly drawn tattoos herself lumbered into the room from a connecting hallway that led to the bedrooms and a bathroom. I could actually feel the vibrations rattle through the flooring as she aggressively entered the room. She was in her usual foul mood and wanted to see who was of such poor character that they would call upon Clyde for a social call.

Clyde and Loretta's son Joey followed in tow but he was somewhat timid in his entrance. He was about six foot tall and weighed close to two hundred fifty pounds soaking wet if I had to take a quick guess. He might have been in his mid twenties. He was shirtless but was wearing denim work overalls which were heavily stained with grease and oil from probably doing mechanic work on vehicles. He suffered from some affliction that might have been undiagnosed autism or possibly something more severe. He was very childlike in his speech and I don't think he had been in school for much of his life.

Whenever we were forced to arrest Clyde or Loretta on a typical Friday night domestic call, Joey always remained calm and never interfered with the officers. He had grown up in the chaos of the home for too long and probably welcomed some peace and quiet when one of his parents went to the clink for a few hours.

The Domestic Violence Unit was always notified from the scene and would advise if the charges were misdemeanor or felony depending on the severity of the injuries that the officers had observed. The person who was always "less" injured was usually determined to be the suspect and conversely the person with more visible injuries was almost always designated as the victim. It was usually a coin toss with Clyde and Loretta on who went to jail each time.

I tried to greet Loretta with a polite salutation and smile but she was already furiously focused at Clyde and ignored my presence.

"Your useless one armed ass should be fixing the Goddam air conditioning and not hanging out with your hood rat friends. It's hot as balls in here. Look at your son. He's sweating all the God damn time," she yelled in a deep throaty voice.

"Woman, it's going to take me all day, but I'm going to slap the stupid out of your fat ass if you don't get the fuck out of my face," he retorted in anger.

In the history of trailer park domestic fights, Loretta and Clyde were almost legendary and incomparable to any other competitors for this honor. "Do it. Do it! Come on. Get out of that chair. I dare you cock sucker," Loretta challenged Clyde in a threatening voice.

"Loretta, you're crossing the line. I'm warning you. I'm going to put my size 13 up your ass in a hot minute," Clyde threatened back.

"I'll knock the last three teeth out of your dirty head, you imbecile," she warned as her forehead began to develop beads of sweat.

I interjected as politely as I could indicating Tammy and I could leave and just come back at a later time when it was more convenient.

Clyde refused on principal to concede to Loretta, "No, no, sit down, Dewey! You're guests! Loretta is leaving! She gets her ugly head worked on at the hair salon on Tuesdays."

Loretta seemed to deflate as quickly as she had become enraged and started to compose herself somewhat, "You're lucky I'm getting my hair done or I'd donkey kick your dumb ass out of this house. When I get back that AC better be cranking cold air."

I honestly thought the situation was coming to a close with Loretta leaving for her hair appointment but Clyde wanted to impress his new guests with his authority over his castle. He stood up and kicked the box fan from the window sending it into the back yard, "There! It's fixed Loretta! I can feel the cold air now!"

Loretta was neither impressed nor intimidated. She left the trailer, slamming the screen door behind her. Clyde returned to his well worn recliner as Joey sat in a folding chair near the kitchen.

I tried to break the tension in the room, "Women, right? Can't live with them. Can't put em' in cages."

Clyde chuckled, "Joey, get us three beers."

I played a game in my head trying to guess what brand of beer Joey would bring for us to enjoy. I thought Keystone Light was a possibility but was corrected when he handed out crisp cold Natural Lights instead.

Tammy drank her beer with two or three large gulps and a quiet belch of appreciation. Clyde's anger subsided from Loretta's insults and I could tell he was glad she was gone and now had company to listen to him talk about the war, his missing arm and other topics of interest.

Clyde again insisted I had a familiar face and in return I joked telling him that Tammy had told me all "white people looked the same." He produced another violent raspy smokers laugh from Tammy's observations.

We continued talking and I let Clyde finish his beer and start on a second before I moved the conversation towards dope, "Hey Clyde, I know you're cool so I'm just going to ask you, man. Tammy and I want to party tonight and we're looking to score some ice. You know anybody around here?"

"Shit, Dewey, why didn't you say so, son? I got some crank that will make you want to bend Tammy over for three days straight," he exclaimed with unusual pride.

"Oh, momma like that, let's get started on that, Dewey," she bellowed, almost choking on a swallow of beer.

I gave her a sideways glance of irritation, "That sounds great Clyde, I got like 50 bucks."

Clyde instructed his son, "Joey, go to my closet, bring me my red Air Jordans."

Joey left the room to find the pair of shoes containing Clyde's stash. For some reason, people hide dope in shoes. It sucks for the cops because we have to search through every pair of shoes in the house to find it.

I had finished my beer and was ready to receive my gold star from Shale if I could pull off the buy from Clyde. "You lose your arm in the war, Clyde?" I asked filling the pause in our conversation with hopefully a war story about his missing arm until Joey returned with the shoes.

"Nah, I flipped my motorcycle on I-70 near Arrowhead Stadium. I was pretty drunk. I had a BAC. of point two one," he boasted as if there were accolades and recognition for high BAC. levels. I wasn't impressed as I had arrested guys with higher levels than that who could still ride their motorcycles. I was hoping he would've told us a crazy war story involving his arm.

"But this arm here, strong as an elephant trunk. I can beat every guy in this park at arm wrestling," he exclaimed.

I knew immediately at that moment without any reservation or guesswork Tammy would open her fucking big mouth and challenge Clyde and I to arm wrestle each other.

"Shit, my man loves to arm wrestle. He's never been beaten. Dewey looks like a Jerry's kid without his shirt on but he's got crack head strength. He's strong," she explained.

"Um, hey, Tammy," I began to address her.

"Challenge accepted Mr. Dewey. Roll them sleeves up, boy," Clyde excitedly demanded in preparation for the match.

Joey returned with the pair of shoes but I knew I would have to engage in this debacle before leaving the trailer with my bag of dope.

Clyde and I relocated to a dirty card table set up in the living room. I thought we would arm wrestle first before the dope deal but Clyde reversed the order removing a filthy sock from one of the shoes. He retrieved a clear plastic bag containing around two or three ounces of crystal meth from inside the sock. It was a decent stash for a person like Clyde.

"Get my clock Joey, from the on top of the fridge," he ordered.

"Clock" was street slang for the small digital scales used to weigh out dope. I placed fifty dollars on the table. I was impressed as Clyde weighed out my dope and bagged it for me using his one arm and his mouth to help. I think he wanted to impress me with his independence despite his handicap.

He removed an oddly shaped green glass pipe from the same sock and added a small pinch of the crystals to the pipe so he could smoke before the tournament began. I literally had no idea if meth smoking gave you strength. Maybe he would tear my arm from the socket from his freshly enhanced un-natural meth strength.

He held the pipe in his mouth by clenching his lips together and used his hand to ignite the lighter that warmed the crystals to produce the vapor fumes. I could see the white vapor leave the pipe and travel towards his mouth. His eyes watered a little bit but other than that he didn't change much in his composure.

We gripped hands tightly as Tammy yelled for us to start the match. I put on a theatrical display of intense struggling against his unyielding strength but eventually allowed Clyde to pin my arm to the card table after a few minutes. He was actually stronger than I had imagined for an older one armed chronic drug user in poor health.

Clyde leaned back in his chair and celebrated his win by smoking a little more from his meth pipe.

"Damn, you're right, Clyde. You're as strong as a gorilla," I exclaimed congratulating him.

He slapped his hand against his gut while boasting, " Still unbeaten, Miss Tammy. You see your boyfriend. I almost tore his arm off."

"Yeah, but he got them little bitch arms," she clarified while trying to stifle her giggling.

Clyde wished us well and assured us that we would make love for hours under the heated passionate blanket of meth induced ecstasy. He invited us to return any time we needed more dope and I believed he sincerely hoped we would return as he enjoyed our company for the afternoon.

We thanked Clyde and as we left, I remembered to specifically thank Joey for the beer.

In his childlike voice he responded, "You're welcome. Come back soon."

Tammy and I entered the Jeep and departed the area. As we exited the park, I turned off the rat phone and found my radio in my backpack. As was customary, I broadcast to all of my back-up units, that it had been a "good deal."

For the first time since coming to SNU, Shale gave a brief congratulations to me over the radio. I broadcast a short reply of "thanks" but was careful in my tone to show everyone that I had simply done my job as I would do repeatedly again each day with the same level of success.

Tammy and I met Shale at a parking lot. I only had a few test kits left for cocaine, heroin and marijuana so he brought over one specifically for meth. We were required to field test any drugs we obtained regardless of how purported the substance was in appearance to be a controlled substance. The test results were also required to satisfy the probable cause affidavits for the subsequent search warrants where the drugs were obtained from.

We shipped our drugs to a laboratory for detailed chemical analysis but the process usually took a couple weeks to get the certified results back. The window of getting a warrant from an undercover buy was always less than 48 hours. The test kits allowed us to obtain the warrants before the window of allowed time expired.

Shale's test kit was a small pouch of transparent plastic that contained two glass ampules inside of it. The pouch itself was about the size of a book of matches. Each ampule contained a liquid that in combination with the other, produced a bright purple color when the mixed liquids came in contact with any Methamphetamine.

Shale dropped a small crystal into the pouch and sealed the top. Shale squeezed both glass ampules inside the pouch which broke open and mixed with the meth crystals. As expected, the liquid quickly turned to purple.

SNU had two administrative plain clothes detectives who were not assigned to working undercover but instead helped prepare the warrants for the undercover narcs. These same detectives also interviewed our "in-custody" arrests who were picked up during the raids or were arrested during our undercover street corner buy-busts.

I worked with one of the detectives named Doug Nevelle. He was a great guy who processed my warrants quickly within usually an hour or two. The endeavor was streamlined and repetitious for Doug and I. After finishing a house buy, I would write up a few paragraphs of notes and the results of my quick drug field test kit to turn over to him. Doug would type out a quick affidavit and present it to a state judge. I informed Doug the trailer was a very special warrant for me with sentimental attachment due to my history with the occupants. He said he would wrap the warrant up like a king's royal scroll to present it to the judge.

Shale took his leave of us and told us he was heading back to the office. There wasn't enough time to get into another house as our tactical back-up car was only available for another 30 minutes before it was being obligated to another narc's house call.

I didn't mind as I was tired and wanted to call it a day after my adventures with Clyde. Tammy and I started back towards her apartment in midtown and had a 30 minute drive ahead of us before we arrived.

I told Tammy I felt dirty after sitting in Clyde's trailer and needed to go home and clean myself for a week. She laughed and admonished me for letting an old, one armed meth-head beat me so easily at arm wrestling. I explained to her that it was all part of the charade of my character to help the deal go smoother. She just laughed and grabbed another cherry cigar from the glove box on the ride home.

CHAPTER 9 - THE SUPER FRIENDS

The majority of police corruption cases are investigated by the FEDs, specifically the FBI. Sometimes the state police are involved in the investigation as a counterpart and support element to the FBI. If the corruption case involves large quantities of drugs or money from the sale of drugs, the DEA can also have jurisdiction to participate in the investigation as well.

The cases always require well documented and recorded evidence of the crimes being committed by the accused officers. Cases that are brought to a prosecutor with only historical eye witness testimony are usually set aside for further development but are not submitted for prosecution. It is literally necessary to catch corrupt officers in the act of stealing evidence, namely drugs and money, for a jury to convict them.

The cases are complex and usually take years and not months to complete. It's not only damaging to the department's reputation but if the level of corruption is more egregious, it's equally embarrassing to the city as well.

The informants who assist in these types of investigations are almost given exclusive immunity from prosecution of any crime they committed while co-conspiring with the accused police officers.

In order to steal large sums of money from traffickers, it's necessary to know where to find the money and how to steal it. It's difficult for law enforcement personnel without having more extensive knowledge and training to have the ability to pull off these types of crimes successfully. The majority of complex police corruption cases prosecuted in the United States have been cases involving drug units and detectives who are trained in surveillance and have knowledge of drug trafficking methods.

What makes the cases of police corruption so difficult to identify is that all of the victims being robbed are drug traffickers themselves who make their money from the distribution of their illegal drugs.

It's difficult to report to the authorities someone has stolen money from you that was obtained from selling heroin everyday. Dealers steal from each other every day in every city in America relentlessly. In their minds there was not much difference between being robbed by another dealer or a corrupt cop. It was just the cost of doing business.

In April of 2002, a late 90's model Coachmen Catalina RV had left its point of origin in Bison, Oklahoma, a small town of less than one hundred people. Bison sits off of Interstate 81 approximately six miles south of the city of Hennessy and northwest of Oklahoma City.

The Coachman was properly registered with Oklahoma tags under the name of the registered owners, Walter and Joanne Gardner. The Gardners kept the RV interior clean and tidy, free from any travel gear cluttering the floor. The vehicle was a light beige color which would show the grime of dirt and dead bugs after driving on the highway so Walter was meticulous at washing it every few thousands of miles or so.

Walter was medically retired from truck driving and in declining health from obesity and years of sedentary driving which had led to the onset of degenerative disc disease. He had once been able to drive for 12 to 14 hours at a stretch as a truck driver without any discomfort but now could only pull about six to eight hours before needing to stop and recuperate. He found the best way to ease the pain of his deteriorating spine was in a swimming pool. The weightlessness of the water was immediate relief for him with the addition of a few opiate pills. There were plenty of RV camper parks that offered swimming pool amenities with the hook up services for RV camping.

Joanne had a small home business which had been placed on hold as they made their trip together. Walter and his wife of 25 years had lived primarily in Oklahoma but had also lived briefly near Wichita, Kansas and Joplin, Missouri.

Their trip on the surface was unremarkable and not particularly interesting as they told people they were visiting friends in Iowa City and were planning a few sightseeing stops along the way.

If anyone had followed their route closely, it was an unusual journey that followed a counterclockwise loop of travel with stops made in St. Louis, Missouri, Fort Wayne, Indiana and the city of East Chicago. The RV would travel southwest from Chicago making one stop in Kansas City, Missouri before the Coachman traveled to Tucson, Arizona where it would stop and unload between two and thee million dollars. The money was concealed in two separate hidden voids inside of the vehicle. The first void was under the cabin seats that surrounded the eating table near the front of the vehicle. The second void was much larger and located behind a false wall at the rear of the vehicle.

The vehicle was purchased for the Gardners by a drug cartel affiliated criminal organization. There were actually two large RV's purchased for them but the Gardners were only in possession of one of the vehicles at any given time. The second RV was kept at another undisclosed location until it was needed.

The Gardners followed an established route and schedule while making a few check-in phone calls along the way with people using alias names who would make sure the Gardners were not having any issues or being followed during the trip. The Gardners didn't ask questions and rarely met their contacts.

The stop in Kansas City was to pick up the smallest bag of money out of the four stops. The bag in Kansas City usually contained around three or four hundred thousand dollars of bundled cash which was easily concealable inside of a single gym bag. However, when the RV reached Kansas City, it was at its fullest capacity since it was the last of the four cities where the money was picked up.

The round trips were made three or four times a year and were very rewarding for the Gardners as they were paid $25,000 per every million in cash they successfully smuggled across the US to the southern border.

Unfortunately, as they approached Kansas City on the last trip they would make, their arrival was anticipated. It was even more unfortunate that the location of their arrival was also known by a few select members of SNU.

Red provided Shale with the arrival time of the RV. The last bag for the couriers to pick up in Kansas City was Red's own money. He was stealing from his own sources though the cover of the Super Friends. Red would not only pay off his debt to his sources but would get it back along with half of the entire load as agreed upon with Shale.

The risks were absolutely minimal. Surveillance units would follow the RV out of the city after the bag was picked up. The surveillance units would notify a marked unit to conduct a routine traffic stop of the RV outside of the city on Interstate 35 traveling south. The stop would be made on a remote stretch of the highway near Ottawa, Kansas where there was little presence from other law enforcement agencies. Even if there were other agencies in the area, they would only see a highway traffic stop being conducted as was done dozens of times every day on I-35.

The Gardners would be detained for a few minutes while their vehicle was searched and the money seized. Millions of dollars of untraceable money would be confiscated after which the Gardners would be simply sent on their way to try and explain to their people what had happened.

Shale would assemble the Super Friends to pull off the job for which he believed five people would be enough to do the job.

Throughout the years, Shale used coercion, fear and greed to recruit confederate officers within the department to assist him with supplementing his retirement income. Some of his co-conspirators were people

Shale had caught doing something illegal or out of policy at which time he simply helped them cover their tracks for a favor at a later time.

Once the relationships between Shale and an officer had been consummated with what Shale referred to as "side projects" of stealing evidence, there was no turning back the events. They were now the keepers of each other's secrets.

Anson had been caught by Shale early in his arrival to SNU selling dope in his off hours to compliment his police salary. Shale used an informant who flipped on Anson to make a recorded phone call and then a small controlled heroin buy from Anson. It wasn't enough to get any real jail time but Anson knew at the very least, he'd lose his job and land a felony conviction when Shale called him to his office and played the recorded call.

Anson could hear his own voice bragging about the quality of his dope and quoting the price per gram of the heroin he could provide. It was interesting how Anson knew the risks of talking too much on the phone and yet provided permanent evidence in explicit detail of his drug sale.

Shale knew he now owned Anson and could use his expertise on the streets more than the other Super Friends. Anson proved to be capable of doing more of the heavy lifting with certain types of jobs that couldn't be asked of the other Super Friends.

Another Super Friend was Ernie. Ernie grew up without a father and had been arrested a few times as a juvenile. Shale was fond of Ernie's single mother when Shale was a young patrol officer working in Metro Patrol. Shale took on a father role for Ernie and helped his family with legal assistance to clear enough of Ernie's juvenile record to get him a job at the police department. Ernie worked as an intern in the police garage for two years.

Ernie stayed out of trouble at the police garage and then transitioned to a job working in the jail. After working for a year and a half in the jail, Ernie was accepted into the police academy.

Shale, of course, took care of the finances for Ernie and his mother with the early smaller side projects of his career. Ernie was more loyal to Shale than any of the other Super Friends. They were more family than associates.

Netta was the easiest of the Super Friends to recruit. She had developed a drug habit and was taking bumps from her own buys. She had failed a random drug test at SNU and was an easy "pick-up" for the team. Shale offered her an endless buffet of complimentary drugs and the opportunity to keep her job.

The other two Super Friends were old timers still in patrol who had worked with Shale during his early time on the road. They were train wrecks of cops who had weathered every storm possible from hundreds of citizen complaints to questionable shootings without losing their jobs. They were both permanent wagon drivers. Charlie Lawson worked at Central Patrol on the midnight shift and Dan Hirst worked at South Patrol on the day shift.

Shale never met with the Super Friends as a group, only holding private individual sessions with each person to brief them on their responsibilities.

Shale, Anson, Netta and Ernie were the plain clothes surveillance units to cover the RV's arrival and departure while maintaining continual visual surveillance. Communications were to be conducted only through "burner" Nextel walkie talkie cell phones and not through radios or conventional cellular phone calls. The Super Friends were careful not to bring their work and personal cell phones on side projects to prevent the evidence trail of cell tower usage. It would be hard to explain to a jury why your personal cell phone hit off a cell tower in Ottawa, Kansas near site of a million dollar robbery.

Charlie and Dan would handle the traffic stop using a black Crown Vic with emergency lights. Once the occupants were removed, Ernie would arrive at the stop and help with the search of the vehicle and removal of the contraband.

In the early afternoon, the Gardners pulled into the parking lot of a Home Depot store on Bannister Road next to Interstate 435 in Kansas City, Missouri. The lot was full of cars which made surveillance not much of a chore for Shale's narcs.

A gray Ford F-150 pick-up truck occupied by a single black female driver arrived a few minutes later, parking in the same row as the RV but a few spots closer to the store. The woman carried a duffel bag from the bed of the truck and handed it off to Walter with little or no conversation. Walter took the bag and entered the RV quickly closing the door behind him.

Fifteen minutes had passed until Walter re-appeared in the driver's seat and then departed in the vehicle from the parking lot towards I-435. Fifty miles away, Charlie and Dan were together in the Crown Vic at exit 187 of I-35, waiting for the arrival of the RV.

Shale gave a small transmission through the Nextel walkie talkie to Charlie and Dan indicating the "box" was en route to their location.

The RV, as expected, traveled west on I-435 until it exited onto I-35 south where the vehicle reached Ottawa almost exactly one hour later.

Joanne was the first to see the emergency lights of the patrol car behind the camper. She was siting at the table facing towards the rear of the camper putting a puzzle together on the table.

"What's wrong?" she asked Walter with a concerned voice.

"I don't know, I wasn't speeding," he assured her.

The large vehicle was able to pull over on a wide shoulder and was not in danger of the passing traffic which was light. Both officers exited their vehicle and walked to the front of the vehicle with one officer on the passenger side and the other at the driver's window.

"Can I help you, officer?" asked Walter.

"Step out for a minute, sir, need to speak with you," Charlie instructed.

As Walter walked to the passenger side door past Joanne, he told her not to worry and to stay inside the camper.

Walter searched his brain for the possible reasons for the stop but was interrupted in thought with cold instructions to turn over his driver's license. Charlie was the only officer of the two who spoke during the encounter.

"Where you coming from?" Charlie asked.

"We spent the week with my wife's sister in Raytown. We're heading to Branson now. She likes all them shows down there. The Dolly Stampede is her favorite. I just go for the food if you can't tell. You guys ever been there?" Walter asked as all the blood had left his face and his heart was racing.

"You mind if we take a look at your rig?" Charlie requested.

Walter fumbled for words and thought it would be best to play it friendly as perhaps they were just checking for equipment violations and if even if they were looking for more, they would still need to find the hidden spots in the camper. He forced himself to breathe as he was feeling light headed. Charlie asked Walter if he and Joanne would wait outside of the camper while they looked inside.

As Joanne stepped outside, Walter was quick to assure her they would be back on the road soon. They stood together next to Dan as Charlie entered the vehicle. It was at this time Ernie arrived in a dark colored Chevrolet Lumina sedan and parked behind the Crown Vic. He exited and was dressed in plainclothes carrying a small bag of tools which included a cordless electric drill. He had a badge on a chain around his neck to identify himself and quickly walked past Dan and the Gardners into the camper.

After twenty minutes passed, Ernie exited the RV holding the first large heat sealed bag of money. It was the first of ten bags found under the seats around the table. He made trip after trip placing the bags of money into the trunk and back seat of his Lumina. Water tried to console Joanne who was crying loudly.

It was only another ten minutes before the second void of money was located in the false wall at the rear of the trailer. The bags of money completely filled the entire trunk of Ernie's car and much of the back seat. Almost three million dollars had been located and removed in under forty-five minutes.

Joanne was visibly shaking and asking if they were going to jail. Charlie exited the RV and approached Walter. Charlie instructed Joanne to wait in the RV and assured her that no one was going to jail today. She slowly walked to the camper glancing back at Walter as she entered.

"Listen, guys, she doesn't know anything. If you take anyone to jail, it's me. I'll go with you. I'll cooperate completely if you just leave her out of it," Walter pleaded in a low voice so Joanne could not hear the details of his proposition.

Charlie and Dan's eyes were concealed behind dark tinted sunglasses which made it difficult for Walter to gauge their reaction to his requests. Charlie handed Walter's drivers license to him and placidly said, "You're free to go, drive safe."

A very strange feeling came over Walter. He had seen a lot of things on the highway over the two decades of his travels throughout the country and was seasoned enough to know something was adversely wrong with his situation aside from losing three million dollars of cartel drug money.

It now registered with Walter that the neither of the officers was wearing a name tag or had identified themselves in any way. Their eyes were concealed behind sunglasses and only one of them spoke with minimal conversation for this type of encounter. Walter was normally asked many more questions on his prior routine traffic violations. He was not in handcuffs and was not even questioned whatsoever about the source of the money.

Walter now had a very serious issue significantly more grave than any threat of incarceration. Upon checking in with his contacts after the stop, he would have to explain what had happened to their money.

Any time money is seized by a local cop, a sheriff's deputy, a state trooper, a detective or even a federal agent, the seizing official is required to leave forfeiture claim paperwork of the seizure or a inventory receipt of what was taken so that the possessor of the currency can make a claim to it in a court hearing. The burden falls to the possessor of the money and not the government to show the legitimate source of the funds. In some cases, a prosecutor can reach a settlement agreement with the defendant's attorney to release some of the money back.

Any time contraband was taken from a courier on the road, members of the courier's criminal organizations always asked for the driver's paperwork, the police reports. Some organizations have lawyers retained to inspect the paperwork to confirm the validity of the law enforcement stop and seizure.

If a courier was legitimately stopped by law enforcement and contraband was seized, it was a forgiven cost of doing business if the courier presented his paperwork to his handlers. If the courier did not have any type of police report or receipt it was immediately a debt owed by the courier.

The drug cartels quickly distanced themselves from lower level drug couriers who were caught with drugs. Any association to them and the drugs they were caught smuggling could bring the cartel members into the same conspiracy indictment as the couriers.

Losing money was a much different conversation within the organization. Someone was always accountable for significant losses of cash.

Walter gently touched Charlies arm, "Officer, please, I need some type of receipt or a police report, okay?"

"It's in the mail, Mr. Gardner," Charlie said with a very small smirk.

"Hey man, I'm not fucking joking here, guy! I need that fucking paperwork, this is about my family. You understand that?" he desperately pleaded as his eyes watered and the sides of his mouth were filled with cotton saliva. "Please, I'm begging you, we're supposed to bring that to Tucson in two days."

Charlie, a large man with a sturdy frame who had played defensive tackle for his college football team stood very close to Walter who was child like by physical comparison. Ernie had already left the scene of the stop with all of the money.

"Walter Gardner, you and your wife Joanne Gardner are free to return to Bison, Oklahoma. Have a safe trip," Charlie carefully advised.

Walter didn't need to plead anymore or throw any more tantrums on the side of the road asking for police reports. It was a rip. It was nothing more and nothing less than just a quick robbery of un-reportable drug money.

Maybe they were dirty cops and maybe they were just bad people who robbed drug dealers for a living. The large officer's concluding farewell was simply coded reference of knowing the identity of Walter, his wife and where they lived. Walter knew the people in the uniforms could kill him and his family as easy as the cartel could. He returned to the camper and by the time he returned to the driver's seat, the patrol car was already gone.

Anytime a Super Friends' side project was completed, the spoils were taken to an apartment leased under the name of a relative of Ernie's mother. No one lived at the apartment, which contained only a few pieces of furniture. A money counter, packaging materials and few handguns with obliterated serial numbers were kept in a back bedroom.

Ernie and Shale were the only two people who knew the location of the apartment and referred to it by coded reference as "the castle." It was located in downtown Kansas City, Missouri near the Westport area. The castle was a second story apartment unit accessible by a rear, alley facing staircase in an area occupied with mostly commercial and non-residential buildings. It was difficult to find even if you knew the location of the apartment. Its location had been carefully selected for its counter surveillance advantages. It was nearly impossible for anyone to conduct surveillance of the apartment sitting on the street without being spotted quickly by Shale or Ernie.

The door of the castle was heavily fortified with an armor guard gate on the exterior side of the door. Once inside, the occupants could use two wooden crossbeams as additional deterrent from exterior breaching. There were exterior CCTV cameras to cover each side of the building. It was not possible to approach from any side of the building to include the alleyway without being seen on the interior surveillance system.

The castle was used to store money and drugs and was never used for anything other than this purpose. Ernie and Shale stayed inside of the castle only long enough to conduct their illicit business before leaving.

Shale and Ernie arrived to the castle as the sun was starting to set. The shadows between the buildings gave some camouflage in the alleyway as they took turns quickly carrying the bags of money up the stairs into the apartment. They dragged the money to the back bedroom and cut the plastic bags apart to separate the stacks of money. The money was compiled in mostly street denominations of twenty and ten dollar bills which made the haul extremely voluminous. Shale and Ernie ran two money counters simultaneously throughout most of the night to get an exact count. There were three or four counterfeit bills which were caught by the money counters, removed and discarded.

Shale was a thief, a drug dealer, a liar and a corrupt cop but he was an honest merchant when it came time to spitting up the bags. He calculated the Gardner load to the last dollar of $2,837,420. Red took half off the top; $1,418,710. The rest was an even split among the Super Friends with an additional management bonus paid to Shale.

The cash was repackaged into new vacuum heat sealed plastic bags using a "food saver" sealing machine. From this point, Shale would only transport one person's bag at a time from the apartment to another location where the recipient was instructed to wait.

Shale was an expert at counter surveillance and pulling "heat runs" to confirm he was driving unmonitored. Shale inspected the underside of his vehicle weekly for "ticks" which were electronic GPS tracking devices magnetically attached to the underside of vehicles. They were used by the FEDs primarily but some larger departments could afford the devices.

Shale always squared city blocks in random patters to see if any vehicles were seen more than once behind his vehicle in a period of at least 30 minutes when he was traveling with contraband or was en route to meet an associate. He was meticulous and always planned each meeting with a window of 30 minutes to conduct his counter surveillance before arriving. He would sometimes call as he was arriving to quickly change the meeting location by a block or two to see if any additional cars traveled from one spot to the other following the person who Shale intended to meet.

It took several days to get everyone's money to them but Shale's caution was worth the wait as he always kept everyone safe and well paid without detection.

No one asked how much they would receive and it was understood to never discuss with another Super Friend how much they were being paid.

CHAPTER 10 - EXTRACTION

I was starting to miss Country around the cave. He had only been gone for a week having been promoted to sergeant within one of the traffic units. It was unusual to see him now after he had cut off his beard and long hair to which I informed him he looked like a "square" now.

Everyone at SNU gained 15 pounds aside from me. It was a combination of smoking, eating fast food a lot and not working out as much from the long hours we worked. Whenever someone returned to wearing their uniforms after being in SNU for a year or two, their uniform had oddly shrunk around the midsection. We laughed and simply called it the "SNU 15."

In my years of working narcotics from SNU to the DEA, the rules of handling informants has never changed. Informants technically worked for the department or agency but they were loyal only to their handlers.

No matter what you did in working narcotics, you never stole someone's informant. You would steal other peoples cases but not their informants. This was taboo and I had never seen it or heard of it happening. We would lend informants to other detectives for certain cases where they were needed but they always returned back to the original handling investigator at the end of the day.

If you had an informant who made you a rock star then you took care of that informant in return. If it was Christmas and they needed a few extra bucks for presents for their kids, you threw in a little extra in their pay buckets. You did little things to show them they were appreciated and in return they kept feeding you information from the streets.

Country had inherited a superstar informant, a man named Reggie who had been passed down through four generations of SNU detectives to include Skinner. Reggie had originally worked with the Kansas City Drug Unit which was a squad led by Sgt. Tyra Benedict. The Drug Unit worked exclusively with the FBI and the DEA on larger long term cases. We rarely worked with them unless we were sending them a lead or they needed one of our detectives to help temporarily with surveillance on a case. They didn't want anything to do with SNU and most of us didn't even know where their office was located.

Some of the SNU detectives attempted to get into Tyra's unit but he was very particular to hand-pick her detectives and rarely took unsolicited applications.

Reggie had problems working with a detective in the Drug Unit and hated Tyra. He refused to work with her squad and was subsequently picked up by SNU as an informant. When Tyra found out about Reggie's change of teams, she became even less fond of SNU, if that was possible. Reggie was definitely a first round pick of informants. He could knock out ten houses in a week without really trying. He made his handlers look like rock stars and was well rewarded by the department. I knew it was an honor to be given an informant of Reggie's abilities. Some of the other senior narcs griped a bit about the trade off but there was nothing they could do. It was Country's decision to make.

Reggie was black man in his late 40's of average height with a lean to medium build. His hair was short with a decent fade on the sides. He had a well trimmed goatee and wore a fitted Pittsburgh Pirates cap on most occasions. His biggest indulgence were nice clothes. He dressed impeccably, wearing designer jeans or pants and wore sneakers with a "just out of the box" appearance. If he found a stain on his clothing or a visible scuff on his shoes, it bothered him to the point where he would go home and change immediately.

There were houses in some parts of the city where you couldn't get in based solely on your skin color, particularly if you were white or Hispanic. It didn't matter if you could do the best song and dance, they simply wouldn't let you in because they knew you weren't from the neighborhood.

Reggie had no barriers and could go through any door on a cold call and was usually invited back. He could converse with anyone from a corporate business person to someone on the street corner. He had the "gift of gab" and always made sure each person felt as if their conversation mattered to him and had great value. He effortlessly diffused arguments between other people and kept the mood light whenever he walked into a room. He also possessed the ability to innocuously divert people's conversations in different directions of his choosing if he felt they were moving towards a direction that wasn't to his benefit.

He was a great storyteller. He had grown up running with gangs and had been in prison twice with one of his incarcerations lasting 13 years. He kept the narcs constantly entertained with exciting exploits of his crimes and conquering the ladies when he was a younger, wilder man.

He felt like family at SNU. He took the effort to remember personal details that were shared by the detectives he worked with. He remembered to ask how your sick kid was doing or he made jokes about your sports team, usually being the Chiefs or the Royals.

Reggie looked after the safety of the narc, also. If a house was particularly more dangerous than others and the people inside were assholes he would ask if he could go inside alone. It was never an insult to the skill level of the detective, but we all knew Reggie had the juice to survive in the toughest houses and he didn't want to see the narcs get hurt.

Country introduced me to Reggie and vouched for my good character with him. Reggie was the first person to genuinely like the name "Dewey" and said that one of his best friends as a kid was named "Dewey." Maybe he was making this up to earn some points but I liked him right away regardless.

I was now running two informants full time with Tammy working her charges off and Reggie working for money. Reggie's paperwork took longer to finish as I had to fill out requisition reports to pay him after each buy he did for us.

I had great stats with Reggie bringing me houses he knew about in addition to the tip sheets. Regardless of what your stats were, you still had to draw from the skull weekly. That never changed even if you were leading the squad with the most house buys.

It was in the late summer when I pulled a tip sheet for 3300 Chestnut, Apartment 7. The information stated the person at this apartment sold crack and to "ask for Peanut" to get inside. The anonymous source for the tip also described high levels of foot traffic throughout the day but more frequent at night. The name Peanut seemed odd and I couldn't find an image in my mind of the type of dealer who would use this as an alias. I chuckled as I thought he might have a small peanut like appearance or maybe he had a monocle eyeglass piece like the brand icon "Mr. Peanut."

It was a small, old, two story apartment building built in 1910 and located in a rough residential area that had seen frequent shootings over the summer. It had security armor guard gating over the front and back doors. There were burglar bars covering the ground units' windows and even the outside air conditioning units were secured inside of a reinforced cage to prevent theft of the parts inside.

Despite the security enhancements of the little fortified building, the door locks on the rear side of the building had been disabled allowing entry for the drug customers to flow freely in and out of the common foyer and interior hallway. The building had eight units inside and Peanut's spot was on the second floor.

With the neighborhood being a shooting range and unfriendly to law enforcement types, Shale and six tactical officers suited up and took the raid van out as my back up. For the majority of our house buys, we were supported by two tactical officers in an unmarked Crown Vic patrol car. Occasionally, an entire tactical squad would load up in the van as your backup when you went inside a house in a rough neighborhood or the situation called for extra measures of safety.

It was the second house of the day for Tammy and I. We had finished with a spot at 12th and Monroe which was neither challenging nor particularly interesting.

Tammy had reached a higher level of comfort with me where she was starting to talk more about herself than before and seemed to be making less fun of me now on our travels together throughout the city. It was warm outside but unusually windy. It seemed like the strange mid-west weather that precedes tornadoes with an approaching thunderstorm when it's still hot outside.

Today was special as Tammy provided to me a small glimpse of her life growing up for the first time. I don't know what made this day different from the other days we rode together. I tried to think on the matter so I could repeat any pattern in the future that would trigger her into talking about her past with me again.

She shared with me that she had grown up in the Wayne Minor Housing Projects near 9th Street and Brooklyn Avenue with her mother until she was 14. Her mother was having difficulty with substance addiction which led to Tammy leaving to go live with her aunt in St. Louis. There was a gap in the timeline of when she told me she returned to Kansas City when she was 16.

"What happened? Why did you leave St. Louis?" I asked.

"Mm, mm, I got in trouble with a boy, Dewey," she shyly admitted to me with her cheeks flushed from the memories of that boy.

It was my turn to let out the largest barrel laugh upon hearing this piece of information. I had hoped she would tell me more about this young lad who had caused so much trouble for sweet innocent and young Tammy that she was forced her to leave the city of St. Louis in shame from their love affair. Unfortunately we had run out of time as we had arrived to the apartment building on Chestnut.

The architecture to the building was strange. It didn't match the other building styles I had seen in Kansas City. The top floor was painted in a light color blue that didn't really seem to flatter the house but rather made it appear more odd. The building was in disrepair and some of the windows were simply boarded up instead of being replaced. Much of the trim and wood on the structure was rotted away which increased the unsettling visage of the building with the accompaniment of the strong wind blowing trash and leaves everywhere.

We took our time in getting the rat phone ready. Shale gave his customary flash of the van headlights to affirm he could hear us through the lifeline. I had gotten so tired of Tammy's suggested back stories of us being depraved lovers that I completely stopped asking her before we went into houses anymore. If someone asked us how we knew each other, it was up to me to think of something quickly to say or she would finish the answer for me with a description of our passionate animal-like fornication to the stranger who had asked.

The armor guard gating over the rear door had been damaged badly as if someone had taken a crowbar to it. The regular wood door behind the gate had been kicked in as well where it was no longer a functioning door that could be secured from unwanted entry.

We entered a common foyer area with two benches inside and a broken payphone on the wall. There were also mailboxes on the wall for the tenants. I tried to look for the name "Peanut" on the mailbox marked with the number seven as if it might be found among the other names of the tenants.

The quiet of the hallway was interrupted with the unmistakable sound of a shotgun racking from above us. At the top of the stairs a man was positioned standing watch over the entrance to the apartment like a guard on a prison tower. He was a tall bald black man wearing a gray hooded jacket and had a pair of sunglasses sitting on top of his head. He was kind enough to point the weapon at the wall and not at Tammy or myself. I appreciated his firearm safety and could see the barrel had been shortened making it possible to conceal beneath his jacket if he chose to do so.

"Who's the new white bread, Tammy?" the man asked.

It was strange to see this type of doorman at a dope house but it was incomprehensibly bizarre to me he knew Tammy. I was thankful at this moment that she actually did know everyone in the city.

"He's my man. We need to come up for a minute, see Peanut," she cordially explained.

"That's your man?" he asked making his face slightly crinkle with displeasure from the thought of us together.

"I know, he's ugly as hell, but he's tearin' up dis' ass," she boasted.

He laughed and looked us both over carefully, "Uh-huh. What's your name?"

"Dewey," I responded.

"What?" he asked in a louder voice.

"I'm Dewey," I yelled.

He ran his hand over his face and massaged his chin while deciding whether to allow Tammy and I an audience with the prominent Mr. Peanut, "You're lucky to have a special lady like Big Tammy. Show her how special she is Doody."

I reminded him that my name was Dewey and asked for clarification as to what I specifically needed to show Tammy.

"Give ol' girl a kiss," he instructed.

For a brief second I balanced the decision of being shot or having to pleasure Tammy in the foyer of that horrible place. I looked at Tammy praying she would diffuse the situation with some lifeline of help that would alter the course of our situation. Instead she was childishly sticking her tongue out of her mouth and running it across her lips in a vulgar manner while softly whispering, "Mm-hm, momma like."

I knew there was nothing I could do at this point. I was young and still had a full life to live and being shot to death in that place was not the right choice to make. Maybe I could undergo intense therapy with medications someday to erase the memories of what Tammy was going to do to me. I moved forward towards her, leaned down and clenched my lips as tightly as possible so that Tammy would have difficulty in forcing her tongue into my mouth as I presumed she would try to do. My initial plan on paper was to give her a very small and quick peck pulling away quickly before she was able to latch onto me like a sea squid wrapping its powerful tentacles around a helpless smaller fish.

She sensed my plan and quickly grabbed me in a bear hug before I could physically prepare myself. I was immediately put off balance with my arms pinned at my sides which diminished my leverage and ability in being able to pull away from her. I fell forward, caught in her large embrace and bosoms. I gasped in surprise of her unannounced violent attack which was an unforgivable tactical mistake on my part as she was able to quickly force her large tongue inside of my mouth. I could smell and taste the cherry flavored Black and Mild cigar remnants entering my body from hers like an invading virus. I felt powerless and weak like a small child's doll hanging in the air being held and squeezed tightly by a toddler for what seemed like an eternity. The experience was further consummated with a painful slap from her heavy thick hand on my posterior which sounded like wet leather hitting a hard surface producing a loud and sharp crack echoing through the hall of the building.

Shale's crew were sitting in two bench rows lined against each side of the windowless tactical van. My rat phone was being broadcast over a speaker on the ceiling which could be heard by everyone inside. It was optically a family of large muscular men attired in body armor and tactical gear gathered around the radio listening to an exciting dramatic broadcast of their favorite show, the Tammy and Dewey Adventure Hour. They giggled and snickered like oversized children from what they were hearing.

Shale remained stoic and simply announced over their laughter, "All right, ladies, the doorman's got a shotgun. Stay sharp."

It took the doorman a full minute to clear the tears from his eyes and compose himself from laughing so hard from the entanglement he had witnessed. He concealed his shotgun under his jacket and prepared to present us to the court of Peanut, "All right, come up, you lovebirds."

We ascended the stairs to him at which time he directed us towards apartment number seven at the end of an unlit hallway. It appeared that the majority of units on the second floor were unoccupied as the doors were open or simply missing. I could see as I passed the empty units were littered with remnants of trash and graffiti on the walls. I could tell they were being occasionally used by squatters and addicts.

We reached the door to our unit which was marked with the address documented on our tip sheet. A full minute passed after knocking on the door before a woman answered. She was a dark skinned black woman who was thin but had muscular shoulders. Her hair was a short cropped afro dyed bright blonde to almost white. Dark lined tattoos of flowers and leaves twisting and blooming were visible from her upper arms reaching towards her shoulders and neck. Her left eye was clouded white from an advanced cataract or some other visual impairment. It could've been a strange cosmetic contact as well. She was incredibly beautiful like an exotic runway model from a foreign European country but also seemed equally as dangerous as I could see the handle of a chrome revolver tucked in the front of her pants. It was evident that she had placed it in an uncovered visible position broadcasting to anyone that she presented a threat if provoked.

I fumbled in my thoughts and words still mentally recovering from my violent sexual assault downstairs to now being caught off-guard by this unusual dangerously beautiful woman who didn't look like a "Peanut."

She knew we were junkies and I could see a mattress on the squalid floor behind her with other smokers already gathered. She was still a gatekeeper like the man with the shotgun and had her due diligence to conduct with Tammy and I before we could enter.

"What do you want?" she asked already knowing our intentions. "Is Peanut here?" I asked in almost a forced whisper.

She wasn't looking for a song and dance as was customary at most houses. This was a busy factory of a dope house selling as much dope as quickly as possible to as many people who came through the door. She asked us what we specifically wanted, forcing us to provide our order before being allowed inside.

I asked her for a "twamp" which was a coded reference of asking for twenty dollars worth of crack cocaine. She didn't understand my reference or perhaps couldn't hear my timid quiet voice as I spoke. I increased my volume slightly and clarified that we were looking for a "twenty piece." She asked me for my money and I tried to see if she would allow me to look at the pieces for sale before exchanging money.

Tammy declaratively interrupted our conversation with her sage advice, "Quit playing ya' sideways turd, pay the woman." She was right as I was moving towards getting the door slammed in my face instead of making the exchange happen. I corrected course and pulled a wrinkled twenty from my shirt pocket.

The woman took our money and opened the door further, motioning for us to enter. The apartment was sparsely furnished and as filthy or more as the other spots we had visited. There was a dirty mattress on the floor which provided a more comfortable place to sit than just the floor for the three addicts already in the room.

A black man and woman were sitting next to a white man who was neatly dressed in a waiter's uniform. He was wearing the uniform of a staff server of an expensive four star restaurant located in a downtown part of the city called "The Plaza." He was clean shaven and had a well groomed haircut. He appeared the opposite of what I had seen and imagined addicts to look like from my limited experience of working lower level drug cases. There was not a possibility of him being an undercover narc from some other agency as he was more feverishly smoking from a glass pipe than the other addicts in the room. His eyes were closed as he was heating his pipe with a lighter as we entered.

There was a box fan in the open window which made me think that it was a requirement for all drug houses to have fans sitting in the opened windows during the warm summer months. Thankfully, I didn't see insects and roaches on the walls which made the apartment somewhat more tolerable.

Tammy allowed herself to fall onto the mattress with a clumsy motion which distracted the other addicts for a few seconds before they continued focusing on smoking from their pipes. The black man and woman were sharing from the same pipe, alternating using the lighter to heat the cocaine base to fumes while the other smoked.

I refused to sit on the mattress and instead sat on the floor with my back leaned against a section of the wall. I was close to the door and could see the entire room which I felt was as good as a vantage point as any other.

The woman who had let us in to the apartment exited the room with our money but returned a few minutes later following a man in a wheelchair who had entered. He was possibly Dominican and was in his 60s with long gray hair tied in a pony tail. He looked unhealthy not only from his condition of using a wheelchair but from his eyes which were yellow. He had a brown blanket across his lap and he might have had a colostomy bag at his side but it was difficult for me to tell as I really didn't know how those devices looked or worked. I was confident this man was "Peanut."

Peanut positioned his wheelchair in front of the waiter and began addressing him. He now paused only long enough between inhalations from the pipe to hear Peanut speak.

"Your tab is up. You've been here for two days" Peanut informed him.

The waiter was cocky and without fear which I'm sure was bolstered by the effects of the drugs in his system, "I've spent three hundred in here. I think my credit's good, partner."

I was on the fence whether Peanut's female assistant was as dangerous as she looked or if she was all fluff. She sensed the belligerent attitude of the waiter and began to reach towards her pistol. Peanut quickly put his hand up to discourage any adverse actions from her while addressing the waiter again, "There's no credit here, what else you got?"

The waiter seemed irritated that he now had to stop smoking to engage Peanut more fully in conversation over his tab. He removed his watch and handed it Peanut, "This, my friend, is a genuine Cartier chronometer that retails at five hundred dollars. I think it's waterproof too if you like swim." The waiter chuckled immaturely at his joke which seemed particularly insensitive towards the handicapped condition of Peanut. I'm sure if the waiter wasn't spending $300 dollars a day inside of that house he would've been given a lesson in manners by someone.

Peanut inventoried the watch carefully before handing it to his assistant whom he now addressed by the name Myra. "All right, you got yourself some more smoke," he advised the waiter before moving on to the black man sitting on the mattress.

The next man was twice as obstinate and insulting as the waiter and refused to give any sort of direct acknowledgment to Peanut during their discussion of him loitering too long inside of the crack house. Peanut tried a polite request for the man to leave before the situation was forwarded to Myra to sort out.

The man fallaciously exhaled smoke into Peanut's face while challenging him, "Suck my dick you crippled mother—"

My inquisition of Myra's abilities and temperament were immediately answered as she violently crashed the side of her revolver against the man's head. The sound of the metal hitting the meat of his skull could be heard in unsettling clarity in the room. She moved very quickly and it was difficult to actually see her remove the firearm and hit the man as it was a blurred singular movement to my eyes. As he began to react from the pain of the strike, she placed two of her thin fingers inside of the man's nostrils which seemed to fit without effort. The forced pain compliance of her fingers deep inside of his nasal cavity lifted him from the floor. He slapped her hand from his face which gave her the next counterstrike which was a well placed kick to the center of his chest.

The man was knocked hard enough to fall through the open window pulling the fan outside with him. From seeing the flailing off balanced position of his body as it exited the window, I knew his landing would be painful as he had another fifteen feet to fall from the second story apartment before hitting the ground.

Myra walked to the window to see the man rolling around in the grass moaning and trying to stand. The man quickly recovered under his own power and made his was to another less contentious house to continue his smoking endeavors. This was a barometer of the perils for the life of a junky on the street.

I was alarmed and didn't expect my reaction to be as verbally pronounced as when I exclaimed, "What the hell, man?"

My outburst quickly drew the attention of Peanut, who scuttled his chair towards my position against the wall. I was blocked of any movement from the wall by the proximity of his chair to my legs.

His yellow sickly eyes scanned the name tag of my shirt, "Duh, Dew, Dewey. Let's see boy, you want a twenty piece. I'm sorry about that. Today's been nothing but crazy up in here." He proceeded to pull a clear plastic bag of twenty to thirty individually packaged pieces of crack from deep inside of his pants. He fished around having difficulty retrieving the bag.

"You like my hiding spot? This is a good spot to hide your stones, Dewey" he advised.

He wasn't as clever as he thought he was as every corner dealer in the city hid their bags of dope in the worst spots of their body cavities in an attempt to prevent the cops from finding the contraband.

"Yeah, sure, I guess," I answered, sounding somewhat unimpressed.

Peanut was already aggravated from the prior encounter and had not brought his mindset back to a composed state. My lack of enthusiasm for his idea of drug concealment simply added to his irritability for the day. If I had been a better narc, I would have sensed this and flattered him with a compliment instead of diminishing his idea.

He took offense and boasted that his smoke was the best in the city. He was bothered enough that it unfortunately triggered Myra to also turn her attention to me as well. I knew I was off to a bad start with the both of them.

Peanut asked to inspect my hands to which I responded by asking if I was required to wash my hands before coming to his spot. He was not a particularly smart person but had been on the streets his entire life selling bags of dope and surviving in the most brutal environments. He had enough survival instincts to reach his age which was credit due to him. His ailments were a result of being shot in the abdomen and spinal cord which had not changed the course of his life.

He civilly explained to me the need to examine my hands was for the reason he had never seen a smoker without having dirty blistered fingers. He was on the money one hundred percent. Drug addicts burned their fingers daily while fumbling with lighters stoned and trying to get high in alleys, cars or wherever they could shelter to smoke. My hands were clean and free from any blemishes that marked the harsh conditions of a person using street drugs daily. Once again Shale was correct with the "clean-dirty" appearance of narcs. I tried to correct course again with a simple explanation that I was always careful when I smoked.

Peanut instructed Myra to prepare a "free house piece" for me to smoke so that I cold be vetted as not being a cop.

"Myra, give me your stem and load it," he instructed her.

She pulled a glass pipe from inside her shirt and carefully forced a pliable small piece of crack cocaine against the copper mesh at the end of the pipe.

"Nah, I ain't smoking in here. Give me a good piece that I paid for. Me and my lady are going to party at home tonight. I'm not hanging out here with these people," I stated.

My request was not unreasonable and had worked before in many other houses for myself and other narcs but it was simply more fuel for Peanut's adversarial attitude for the day's problems.

Tammy asked for the pipe so she could smoke it in my stead which was quickly denied.

I knew our situation was deteriorating so it was a good cue for our exit. They could keep our twenty. "All right, Tammy, these people don't want us here. Let's find another roach motel," I announced attempting to stand up from the wall.

It felt incredibly painful when Myra used the revolver against the side of my head as was done in similar fashion for the previous gentleman. The strike landed less on top of my head and more towards the side of my forehead and face. She again moved incredibly quickly to draw the weapon and use it as a blunt force object. I concluded that her speed was attributed partially as a result from repetition training of this type of attack which she used frequently on the addicts. She had carved a decent gash in my skin which bled profusely.

"Leave him alone, asshole!" yelled Tammy from across the room.

Peanut rolled his chair back a few feet to allow Myra to have more space to address my reactions. As Tammy began to stand, I was worried she would attempt to charge Peanut and Myra which would increase our chances of someone being shot.

Myra had her revolver pressed against my head where I could feel the texture and temperature of the barrel against my skin. Peanut had pulled a black semi automatic pistol from under his leg and racked it before pointing it at Tammy. I was thankful she had the sense to maintain her distance when she saw the weapons drawn.

I calmly waved my hand at Tammy to let her know to stand down from making any quick movements and reluctantly asked Peanut for the pipe.

Shale was focused on the conversation from the rat phone when one of his crew interrupted, "It doesn't sound good in there sarge."

Shale acknowledged the situation was deteriorating and instructed everyone to prepare for an extraction. The squad secured their helmets and made quick inventory checks of their weapons in preparation for their approach to the building. Shale began moving the van down the street closer to the building.

If you're going to do anything in life, it's always best to give it one hundred percent effort as my father would tell me. I guess this advice applied to smoking crack cocaine in an effort to save your life. I felt strange holding the glass pipe. It was already warm from Myra providing some heat to melt the cocaine base into place against the mesh filter.

I wondered if I would immediately turn into a crackhead wandering the streets to support my habit or would it take more than one smoking session to make the transformation complete. Maybe this would be my final metamorphosis from Officer Moore to Dewey the pretend junkie and to finally Jeff the real junky.

I refused Peanut's offer of his lighter and used my own. As I applied the flame and inhaled deeply, I could actually hear the sound of small crackles or pops as the drug turned to vapor. This was of course how the drug got its name.

By leaning forward to inhale from the pipe, I now had enough room to reach an ankle bracelet on my right leg. It was crafted to resemble a court authorized electronic tether device that was commonly worn be people on probation or awaiting trial for a crime. It was clever and some guys wore it with shorts so that it was immediately recognizable. It was so convincing that once people saw it, they didn't really question the possibility of you being a narc.

I triggered my extraction request with series of covertly pressed buttons at the bottom of the device. I did enjoy the onset of the effects of smoking crack which were fully felt within ten-seconds after inhaling. The smoke felt sweet as it passed over my tongue. I remember everything in the room began to move very slowly as if time was changing for me. I focused on Peanut's yellow eyes which became intensely illuminated as if he had bright yellow lights behind his eyes. The fear and anxiety left my body completely and I felt excited and relaxed at the same time. I don't know how it was possible to feel emotions that are contrary to each other but it happened in some form in my mind. The euphoria was intense and sharp in my mind. There was nothing delayed or dulled during the process of getting high.

Shale gave loud verbal orders for the squad to proceed with the extraction which had been verified by the ankle bracelet activation. The door of the van was open as it rolled towards the rear entrance of the apartment building. The team quietly and quickly exited in a single file formation without anyone speaking or yelling.

The doorman with the shotgun was descending the stairwell to the first floor when the door opened a few inches allowing three canisters to be thrown into the entryway. He was unsure of what they were as he had never been involved in a police raid where "flash-bangs" were deployed.

One device in close proximity to a person was enough to knock them over from the concussion pressure. The over utilization of three grenades created enough pressure to damage the man's eardrums, break numerous windows within the structure and render him unconscious. Falling unconscious had saved his life as he was unable to retrieve the shotgun which had fallen from his coat.

The team moved past the man and secured his hands with thick plastic zip-tie restraints. The last man in the formation stayed with him as Shale and the remaining members of the raid team ascended the stairwell.

It sounded like a freight train approaching in the distance with the explosions downstairs. The concussion pressure was felt in everyone's chests. Peanut had been around long enough to know what was happening but I don't think Myra knew. She may have though it was part of some rip crew coming into the building shooting guns.

Peanut threw his handgun out of the open window and positioned his chair in the center of the room. He placed both of his hands into the air as the sounds of the team were getting louder.

Another flash-bang was used on the second level which was tremendously loud. Tammy stood up quickly and faced the door. Myra was also facing the door but made the mistake of pointing her small revolver at the door in defense as if this was sufficient force to hold back the tide of Shale's squad.

I was still foggy but I tried to tell Tammy to sit down repeatedly. During extractions or other extremely dangerous situations, it's common for people to experience tunnel vision, the narrowing of visual and auditory information from the senses. It's merely the mind reacting to adrenaline and preparing the body to face a life threatening encounter. If you were lying on the floor, you were less of a threat and could possibly avoid any stray gunfire from the officers who were fighting the effects of tunnel vision themselves.

It seemed virtually simultaneous as Tammy's large frame fell backwards onto the mattress and the door exploding violently into shards of wood and nails from the breach of a battering ram.

Myra was more of a true believer than I had credited her with. She fired several shots of her revolver and was able to put one round successfully into the leg of the number two officer in the stack. She, however, was hit quickly with return fire from a Benelli semi-automatic shotgun.

This weapon did not have a comparable match for the devastating damage it was capable of delivering during close quarter combat inside of a house. The Benelli fired shells each holding eight pellets a piece and was capable of firing two or three shells within a time frame of a second or two without having to rack the shotgun, simply by pulling the trigger.

Myra successfully received two rounds from the shotgun to her chest which was the equivalent of being shot sixteen times. She was deceased before her body fell to the floor but even in death she was able to squeeze the trigger of her weapon a final time sending a stray round into Peanut's shoulder. Peanut yelled in pain and fell from his chair.

The room was quickly secured with everyone being handcuffed. Everyone excluding Myra and Peanut were taken downstairs to meet arriving patrol cars which included myself and Tammy. The room was a crime scene and would be processed no differently than any other homicide scene.

Shale remained with Peanut and spoke with him regarding the unfortunate events that had occurred, "This place is a mess, what happened in here?"

Peanut knew from the quick extraction that Dewey was a cop, "Your boy did this, Dewey and his babysitter, Fat Tammy."

Shale glanced at Myra and reminded Peanut that this was now a pending homicide case for him regardless of who fired the shots that killed her.

"It doesn't have to be that way, does it? Let's talk, Boss. What do you need?" asked Peanut trying negotiate through the intense pain of his wound.

The injured officer was given a quick tourniquet and transported by an ambulance to Truman Hospital. Peanut's dispatched EMS unit was still en route but this information wasn't passed to Peanut who believed Shale was stalling on getting him medical treatment.

Surprisingly Peanut did possess one piece of information which was of interest to Shale. He knew of a weight house with as many as ten bricks of heroin inside of it.

Shale was skeptical of the information, "How would a duster like you know that? No offense."

Peanut coughed loudly but provided answers to try and convince Shale, "She worked for some people who got dope from the people there."

Peanut nodded in the direction of Myra's body, "They're still going strong there. She actually wanted me to find people to rob that place."

"Whose dope is it?" Shale asked.

"The dope is sold to mostly the Gangster Disciples, I think. Some of it goes to bikers in St. Louis or somewhere. The Mexicans drop stuff there. It's their house," admitted Peanut.

Peanut swore to the sky and back that the house was not a fairy tale. He was even forthcoming by mentioning that the water heater in the basement was sometimes used to hide money inside of it.

"Anyone else know about this? The DEA, State Police, your buddies?" asked Shale.

"Nah, this is my get out of jail card I've been keeping for a rainy day. I guess now is a good time to use it, boss," admitted Peanut.

Shale assured Peanut they now had a gentleman's agreement. If Peanut kept his mouth shut about the house and if it was the truth, Shale would in turn dissipate the culpability of Peanut's involvement with the officer being shot in the leg and Myra's death.

Peanut reached out to weakly shake Shale's hand, "84th and Highland, green house on the corner. There's an Olds Cutlass in the back yard."

Tammy and I were taken to another location in the raid van and dropped off. Someone had driven the Laredo where it was waiting for us when we exited the van into an alleyway. I couldn't tell where I was at first but it looked like we were somewhere downtown by the size of the buildings nearby.

Shale was waiting for me and instructed Tammy to wait in the Jeep while he spoke to me alone. I could see her sitting in the passenger seat starting to light up one of her cigars as Shale and I walked further into the alley to remain out of earshot of her and any of the other officers.

I knew Shale was unhappy with having to explain to the chief that an officer was shot during an extraction as he chose to lecture me of how dangerous working narcotics could be. I hadn't really done anything wrong and it was a perfect storm of multiple problems that had led to the situation deteriorating so quickly. Shale did acknowledge he had never seen or heard anything like Myra before. She was a very rare bird that might be seen only once in our lifetime.

Shale offered me the opportunity to return to patrol if I was done with SNU. He had the contacts to get me to the shift and area of my choice. He was careful not to come off as insulting and he couldn't ignore the fact I was putting up more stats between myself, Tammy and Reggie than any other four narcs in the squad combined. If they wanted to play the stats game, I was holding my own in the lead.

Shale returned to the van as Tammy left the Jeep and stood by my side. As he glanced back at us standing in the alley, I yelled to him, "I think I might have smoked crack in there. What should I do Sarge?"

He didn't acknowledge my question, instead entering the driver's seat of the van and leaving Tammy and I alone in the alley. His silence was a message to me that it was my problem to deal with however I chose.

CHAPTER 11 - WEIGHT HOUSE

Reggie and I worked together for three days in a row as Tammy was sick and needed to recuperate for few days from some stomach bug she described. I told her that it would take a bug as big as a bulldozer inside of that belly to take her off her feet. She laughed loudly and told me it was just morning sickness from being pregnant with "baby Dewey." I told her I would check on her the next day or two but I now had to excuse myself to go throw up from hearing her comments.

Reggie refused to ride in the Laredo as it was too filthy for him to tolerate. He drove a 1997 gold colored Chevrolet Monte Carlo which was cleaner than the floors of a microchip factory. Netta and I followed him throughout the city as he traveled between houses knocking out four or five in a day.

Shale refused to allow the informants to use the rat phone. They were on their own inside of houses. If there was a problem, they had to resolve it on their own. There was slim to no chance of Shale ordering an extraction for an informant. He had no problem with waiting until the people inside of a house carried an informant out to the curb in several trash bags.

If we had not heard from an informant inside of a dope house for 30 minutes or more, we would check on them by text message or a quick phone call. It was important for the informant to stay only long enough inside to make the buy and then leave the house.

Reggie rarely stayed longer than thirty minutes in any house he went to. If the house was dry and a resupply was needed, Reggie refused to wait for the source to arrive, instead preferring to just come back at a later time when the dope was available for sale.

After the last house of the day, Reggie asked to meet with me to discuss some information he had come across. Netta asked if she could excuse herself as she needed to get home for a birthday party.

Reggie and I met at a parking lot where I sat with him in his Monte Carlo. I could tell something important was on his mind as he had saved this conversation until the end of the day.

"Boss, I got a guy who's so big they're gonna' promote you to chief when you take this cat down. He's a big, big player," Reggie exclaimed with excitement.

I always laughed when Reggie told me I would be promoted to the Chief of Police from working a great case. I imagined the case being so big and successful to be able to completely pass over the next five ranks to be given the coveted position of Chief of Police.

Reggie talked about his sister Annetta who lived with her "off and on" boyfriend, a man named Desean Hill. Annetta broke up with Desean repeatedly after fights usually about Desean's other girlfriends but always returned to him within a week or two with her kids in tow.

During the breakups, Reggie, always the great listener, received Annetta's confessions of Desean's drug exploits working for his cousin, Antonio Hill. Annetta felt the burden of guilt lessening by confiding in Reggie as he assured her that she needed to do what was necessary for herself and her kids to survive. By the time the conversation had concluded, Annetta was convinced from Reggie's counseling that she was a good and righteous person doing what was needed to protect her children.

Reggie suspected Annetta might have helped Desean pick up a load car or two from the car haulers as she provided information containing more details than Desean probably would have divulged to his girlfriend.

Reggie saw the opportunity to get rid of his sister's drug dealing boyfriend while at the same time earning a decent paycheck from the department.

I caught Shale in his office at the cave and asked if I could brief him on Reggie's information.

I sat in his office and found him in a reasonably good mood as he had gotten off the phone with the captain who had praised him over the squad's great stats for the month.

"Hey Ryan, I met with one of my sources today, Reggie. He's got some good stuff. You ever hear of a guy they call Red?" I asked.

"Red? No, I can't say I know that name. Who is this guy?" he asked.

"His real name is Antonio Hill. He owns Red's Barbecue downtown." I gave him as many details as I could hitting the high points and skipping unimportant details that would slow the momentum of my briefing. I told him about the car haulers and how Annetta had told Reggie that Desean recently picked up a car loaded with 10 bricks of heroin.

I was somewhat surprised at Shale's reaction. He seemed very tepid and neutral throughout our conversation but still was focusing intently on the details I provided.

"Reggie is on board for helping us get to Desean maybe to the point of being able to flip him into Red." I relayed to Shale.

"Okay, what does he have in mind?" Shale asked with an unusual look of concern on his face.

"Reggie wants Desean to go to prison and leave his sister alone in a big way so he's on board to help the police hit him when he's got dope. Desean is a felon with three prior convictions to include a 6 year stretch in state prison. He's got a few guns and dope in a safe in the basement of Annetta's house. Reggie hangs out there once in a while and smokes weed with the both of them. Reggie said he's seen the safe and Desean showed him a big bag of dope inside of it a month ago. Maybe Tyra's squad or the DEA would want to work with Reggie on this and hit the house when it's fat," I suggested.

"Let's keep this at SNU for now and see what pans out. We can always call them later," Shale suggested.

It was unusual Shale had not referred me to turn the case over to the Drug Unit or the DEA as soon as I has mentioned it. This was nowhere close to being a SNU case. We had never worked anything bigger than four or five ounces of dope at a time and now we were discussing a guy moving cars filled with heroin and cocaine. Maybe he was in a beef with Tyra and this was a way to give her the middle finger especially with Reggie providing the information.

I suggested to Shale, Reggie could give us the green light when Desean was sitting on a decent sized bag at the house and we could hit the door. Desean didn't have a job and was usually there alone with the kids when Annetta left for work each day. With Desean being a convicted felon, he could easily catch a decent federal case with what was sitting in his safe. We would just have to sell him on helping us with Red's load cars. Maybe if he was looking at 15 years, he would sever his loyalty with Red.

Shale leaned back in his chair digesting what I had thrown in his lap. He looked at the ceiling for a minute before responding, "All right Dewey, that's not the worst plan I've heard. You mind grabbing me the address for Desean?"

Again, it didn't make any sense to me that this wouldn't be handed over to Tyra's unit or the FEDs but Shale was the boss and I'm sure with his experience he could see farther into the future than I could. I told him I was leaving for the day and asked if I could grab the address first thing in the morning for him.

"I hate to be a boss-hole. You mind grabbing that info for me real quick before you leave? Oh, and Dewey, can you grab Reggie's file real quick, I need to check something?" Shale asked.

I grabbed Reggie's file and my interview notes which listed Desean's address and returned to Shale's office to give him what he requested before leaving for the day.

The following day, Doug was preparing a search warrant for a house located in the 8300 block of Highland Avenue for which Ernie was the affiant for the affidavit. Shale had the Super Friends spend a week doing surveillance on the house provided by Peanut which was astonishingly located exactly where he had described.

The street was quiet and most of the houses were up kept up in appearance with the exception, of course, being the weight house. The house was a single story structure painted forest green with white trim. Each window was opaquely covered, and surrounded by a cheaply constructed fence consisting of white poles with mesh wire strung between the poles. The fence post holes were lazily dug too shallow which led to many posts leaning badly or completely falling over.

An impressively large Rottweiler mix of a dog resembling a small bear was chained in the front of the house. The length of his chain allowed the dog to roam the majority of the front yard and to the driveway. Unfortunately, large dogs encountered on drug raids were introduced to the Benelli if they couldn't be persuaded to allow passage of the uninvited officers.

A small brown minivan without license plates was parked in the driveway backed closely up to the garage door. During the week of surveillance by Shale's crew, the vehicle had left only once to travel to a small corner market a few blocks away. The occupants were two Hispanic males which seemed to corroborate more of Peanut's story.

Ernie's fictional warrant used a fabricated narrative of an informant buying of a bag of weed from inside the house from an unidentified Hispanic male subject. That's all it took to get a warrant for the door of another Super Friend's side project, just a white lie or two.

The warrant was executed on a Thursday morning around 10:30. The two men inside were already awake and sitting at a table in the kitchen. The people who ran stash houses were often almost as low on the hierarchy ladder of drug traffickers as the couriers. It was mentally a very boring job but was extremely dangerous if not taken seriously.

The men would sit in the house for weeks at a time waiting for out of town couriers to arrive with drug loads which were stored in surplus at the house until delivered to customers. The men watching the stash houses weren't the salesmen or the flashy traffickers who made the deals. They received calls on cheap burner phones from a handler who was sometimes in Mexico or another state directing them with coded references to deliver "tools" or "tires" to a customer at a gas station or parking lot somewhere driving a described vehicle. The drugs were quickly exchanged and the men returned back to the house to wait for further instructions.

The danger occurred if a customer had people who could covertly follow the drop off car back to the stash house. At this point a good crew could do the same thing as the Super Friends but they didn't need a search warrant to get inside. Unfortunately, whoever was inside of the house when a crew made entry on a rip usually wasn't left alive to provide details back to Mexico on the identity of the suspects.

During my third year at East Patrol, we had a house like this with four deceased people inside of it. There was a footprint on the front door and shell casings everywhere. The occupants were dispatched exactly where they were found as the intruders entered searching for money and drugs. It upset me as there was a deceased young woman in the kitchen who was cooking when it happened. I have no doubt her boyfriend's occupation was responsible for claiming her life so early and violently.

The men in the house on Highland Avenue enjoyed beer for an early brunch beverage and every other meal for that matter while waiting for a call which was expected before noon. The house was unfurnished aside from a few chairs, a kitchen card table and mattresses on the bedroom floors. Every outlet contained charging cell phones with at least 15 to 20 devices located throughout the house.

The men lived without responsibility to pick up after themselves or clean up the house in any way. There were beer bottles deposited inside of the house by the dozens. The slept, ate, played cards, drank beer, waited for the phone to ring, dropped off bags to people and repeated the process with little variation.

Both of the men were obligated to work at the house stemming from debt problems with people in Mexico. Whether the debts were legitimate or not, the cartels allowed members of the men's families to live without repercussions in Mexico as long as the house in Kansas City was taken care of and staffed for an agreed period of time.

The raid van approached the house traveling north on Highland Avenue. The sliding exit door of the van was on the passenger's side as the vehicle always approached in a direction where the door faced the target location.

The quiet approach by the raid team was of no real tactical use as the giant bear-dog alerted the neighborhood to their arrival. As the team forced entry through the fence blocking the driveway, the dog was sadly disposed of as it was too big and dangerous to negotiate with.

One of the men inside the house attempted to look through an opening in the window blind after hearing the shotgun but had little time to react as the team was already forcing entry at the front door.

The raid team secured the house quickly without much effort or incident as it was a small structure with only two occupants. The men, who spoke only Spanish were positioned sitting in the living room with their backs to the wall and their hands secured behind their backs.

Shale entered the kitchen area and was greeted by the on-scene Sergeant of the raid team, "We're secure. It's all yours, boss."

"Great job. Tell your crew thanks from us," Shale responded.

The Sergeant collected his team and left the house in the hands of Shale and his associates. Shale waited patiently until every officer had left the house before closing the door and inspecting the interior of house for any surveillance camera systems.

Shale placed two cloth hoods over the heads of the two men sitting on the floor and then called his team over the radio to come inside the house. The men spoke a few words of Spanish to each other but had no real knowledge if the hoods were part of routine police procedure for a search warrant raid.

Anson, Netta and Ernie entered through the partially smashed door and were careful with the volume of their voices so as not to be heard clearly by the men detained. Shale instructed Anson to watch the men in the living room while he, Ernie and Netta made their way through each room of the house.

The search of the basement was simple as there were only a few items large enough to conceal and contain contraband. A large plastic storage container under the basement stairs was covered with several blankets. Shale lifted the blankets to discover 16 square shaped bricks of compressed heroin stacked neatly inside of the plastic tub. Each brick was tightly packaged with the normal layers of tape, plastic and pieces of carbon paper.

The Highland house given as a present from Peanut to the Super Friends proved to be a rewarding side project as a kilogram of high purity heroin in 2003 sold for $70,000 at the wholesale price in Kansas City.

Shale inspected the water heater which was not being used as a secreted space for hiding loot. Peanut's information had been only partially correct as bundles of money wrapped in black electrician's tape were instead located in a furnace duct towards the ceiling. The duct had newer tool marks on some of the screws securing the pieces of metal together that provided evidence the men were repeatedly removing and replacing the screws to access the inside of the duct.

The money and drugs were placed together in the center of the room for closer inventory. Ernie cut opened the bundles of currency and provided a rough count for Shale, "Looks like 16 keys and $400,000 boss."

"Not bad for a day's work guys," Shale praised his team.

"What do you want to list on the return?" asked Ernie.

Every court authorized search warrant comes with a back page or "return page" which is used to list an inventory of what's located and seized during the execution of the search warrant. This return page is included for every warrant regardless of jurisdiction at the local, state or federal level. The inventory is returned to the originating judge who signed the warrant for review.

Shale instinctively seemed to always know the correct amount to steal and the amount to recover as evidence, "All right guys, we found 2 bricks and fifty-thousand here today."

The Super Friends kept for the rest for themselves, 14 kilograms of heroin and all of the money minus fifty-thousand. The warrant return listed "two packages of suspected narcotics and $50,000 - US currency."

There was no real chance the two men in the house would protest the theft by mentioning to anyone someone had stolen their extra 14 kilos of heroin and drug money.

Shale placed the requisitioned items in the trunk of his car to be taken back to the castle. Netta and Ernie took the seized evidence listed on the search warrant return back to the cave for a few trophy photos to be taken which was customary after a successful raid.

Shale called for a dispatched patrol car to arrive and transport the two men downtown for booking and arrest interviews in the morning. Shale had almost forgotten to remove the cloth hoods from the men as the uniformed officers arrived outside.

The officers arrived and met Shale at the door to receive his instructions, "These two guys need to go downtown, please. The charges are felony possession. I'll fax the paperwork over in a couple hours. Thanks, guys."

The officers lifted the men to their feet and transported them downtown.

Shale exited the house and attempted to close the door which was too damaged to latch completely. As Shale began to walk towards his vehicle, he paused and curiously knelt down to inspect the body of the deceased massive dog in the yard as it was unusually larger than most of the other dogs he had seen before. Shale read the inscription of the dog's tag which only listed the hand-inscribed name "Guapo."

The bricks of heroin and the money taken from Highland Avenue sat inside of the castle for two weeks for a cooling off period. During this time, Shale personally conducted counter surveillance around the castle, canvassing the area in a three block radius for any possible surveillance units.

If located, the units would almost always be identified by a single occupant sitting in a vehicle with dark tinted windows for long periods of time watching with a visual line of sight view towards the intended target. Shale was unable to detect anything out the ordinary and proceeded with caution to begin transferring the heroin to Red.

Moving dope between two locations is the Achilles' heel of drug trafficking. When drugs are in transit, they are moving across public roadways, waterways or airways which are subject to closer inspection by law enforcement upon detecting the slightest reasonable suspicion.

The popular legal phrase, "Possession is nine-tenths of the law" is an expression indicating ownership is easier to prove if a person has possession of something and is more difficult to prove if the person does not have possession.

There's almost no way to dismiss or explain away the possession of 14 kilograms of heroin if you are caught with the drugs. You are beset with the difficult odds of persuading a jury to not convict you of a crime that has a minimum floor of 20 years in federal prison. You would receive substantially less time in prison for killing someone unpremeditated in a second degree murder case.

Shale and Ernie drove two vehicles in tandem from the castle to their delivery point. Shale was the trail car behind Ernie who drove a rental car which contained the drugs in a duffel bag in the trunk. Shale had his police radio set to the assigned frequency of the precinct for the area he was driving through. He monitored the radio and kept an eye for any tinted surveillance units or any patrol officers looking to cut traffic tickets in the area.

It was always safer to travel through neighborhoods and smaller streets as opposed to larger roadways. It was also safer to pick the busiest time of day during a morning or afternoon rush hour.

Ernie arrived to a parking lot of a midtown strip mall and parked the rental vehicle among a row of cars. Ernie locked up the car and looked around before placing the keys on top of the rear passenger side tire.

Ernie walked two blocks to the East where he was picked up by Shale on a small side street. Shale and Ernie returned to the area of the strip mall and set up in a vantage point across the street at a gas station to watch the vehicle until someone arrived to pick it up.

Shale had previously purchased two burner cell phones and delivered one of the phones in person to Red a couple of days prior. Each phone was dedicated to be used only to contact the other cell phone in regard to the delivery and then both phones were disposed of afterwards. Each separate event between Shale and Red required a new purchase of two throwaway phones.

At any given time, Red had two or three cell phones in his pockets. He kept one personal cell phone used for his restaurant business, talking to family members and close friends. It was a clean phone which was never used for anything illicit. If someone talking to Red on this phone brought up something illegal, Red quickly just hung up the phone on the person without apology.

As the phone vibrated in Red's pocket, it was the only time the phone had received a call since it had been given to him. He immediately knew the call was an alert that the drop car had been delivered and it now needed to be picked up by Desean. Red answered the phone speaking as little as possible to Shale, "Yeah."

"Fourteen shirts, a gray Toyota Camry," described Shale.

"All right, my man is on his way" Red affirmed.

When Shale initially delivered the cell phone to Red, he provided the location of the strip mall on a small piece of paper which was handed over with the phone. By doing this, Shale knew he would not need to verbally provide the location of the strip mall over the phone to Red. In the event someone was listening to the call, the listener would only have half of the coded message which did not include the location of where the vehicle had been dropped.

Shale and Ernie maintained their surveillance of the Camry for an hour until Desean walked to the vehicle from the direction of the mall. Shale was unable to see how Desean had arrived or who had dropped him off.

Desean quickly found the keys on top of the wheel and left the area in the car heading south away from downtown. Shale admired Desean's calm demeanor under the pressure of taking such a big risk on numerous occasions for Red. He was a great worker for Red.

In the dope game, Red was in the top ten of guys for Kansas City but it would still take him two or three weeks to get the load distributed and the money collected in full. The money came in at around one and a half million dollars from which Red took his half. The rest was given to Shale to be divided among the Super Friends how he saw best to do so.

CHAPTER 12 - DISPOSABLE LIGHTER

I started to see why most of the narcs only stayed at SNU for a year or two. It was a job where it was difficult to separate yourself from your work. In uniform, when you finished your shift, you were done for the day. You could unwind and even shut off your phone if you needed some quiet on your day off.

Working narcotics, your phone was never off. It was your little office that rang throughout the night and on your days off with continuous calls from informants giving you information or asking you for money to help get out of jail for some trouble they had found themselves in.

You were always under the eye of Shale to meet quotas each week. He was responsible for keeping numbers up and the SNU tactical raid team as busy as possible closing nuisance houses. If the narcs weren't getting the warrants, the raid teams were just training and not hitting doors. If they weren't hitting doors, the numbers weren't being provided to the command staff and city council as expected.

The stats of the unit were also used as an accounting process for predicting budgetary requirements of the unit. If SNU was busy and knocking down lots of houses, then additional resources and money was needed for the drug unit. If guys were being lazy and it got slow, then it was assumed more money and detectives weren't needed and the resources of the drug unit could be allocated back to patrol. Instead of SNU having 9 allotted detectives, maybe only 5 were needed. There were always carrots and sticks to keep the guys motivated.

The narcs were sometimes called in to assist other investigative units with surveillance of suspects involved in crimes that weren't drug related. I spent a week living in my Jeep following around a guy who worked at a factory during the day and searched for prostitutes in the evening to strangle. It seemed strange as I wondered if we were following him just to watch him pick someone up and then make the arrest after the body was dumped to actually catch him in the act of killing someone. I was relieved the arrest was quickly made through DNA linking him to the bodies and the latter did not occur.

I was not digesting the stress of SNU in any healthy fashion. I simply kept compiling my anxieties and fears to the back of my mind where I would address them at a later time to sort things out.

The shooting on Chestnut was hard to remember for some reason. There were some details that were clearer in my mind than others. I vividly remembering how yellow Peanut's eyes were and imagery of watching

Tammy clumsily fall onto the mattress at the last possible second before the team entered. It seemed funny to me as if she was falling into a swimming pool at some pool party with her friends and wanted to create massive splash of water.

The horrific memories of beautiful Myra seemed distant and foggy and further from the surface than the other details. I remember with sharpness of clarity, images of initially meeting her at the door seeing her for the first time more than the rest where she was a monster beating people and throwing them through the window.

I was not eating well and was starting to drink more. Tammy and I always had our "prop" beers to last us during the day and I would occasionally buy her another one for the ride home. I found myself also grabbing a second 24 ounce can for myself to end the day with. I did enjoy this time with Tammy as we would sometimes end the day sitting at a park for an hour or two smoking cigars and enjoying a cold beer together.

We now had more stories to talk and joke about from our drug house adventures together. I think she was under less stress working with me than in the beginning. She didn't need to work as hard to keep me from doing the stupid shit that would get myself killed as I was learning from my impressively large mountain of mistakes.

I felt more comfortable asking her questions of why things happened on the streets the way that they did. In the beginning, I initially worried our differences and my lack of understanding of the streets might be offensive to her. She had a good sense of humor towards the bad decisions that were "made in the hood" and she herself was still shocked everyday with things she saw and lived through.

I felt somewhat sad at times as I realized our time together would not last forever and we would eventually return to different places. For the time being, I was part of her world only as Dewey and not Officer Moore. I grew so comfortable playing "Dewey" that I was not really recognizable to myself as "Jeff" anymore. My humor and thoughts were more crass and dark now that I was competing with Tammy for vulgarity points and spending more of my time with junkies and dealers than my own family.

I was less judgmental of the people I was with. The Tweetys, the Mike Taylors and the dealers on the corners seemed a few degrees closer to me now. Periodically, I entertained the idea of discreetly smoking a very small controlled amount of crack cocaine to help with my "undercover courage." Maybe in the big picture, the department would reward my initiative of increased productivity if they didn't know I was specifically enhancing my performance with drugs. I had smoked it once and nothing bad had come of it, so then in honesty a few more times would reasonably be okay as well. I could basically stop smoking crack cocaine when I returned to uniformed patrol. Thankfully I decided against this horrible decision and to not follow through with it.

After I had debriefed Shale with the information I had received from Reggie, the moods between myself, Anson and Ernie began to cool somewhat. I don't think the events were related but the changes were observable. They were immediately indifferent and distanced themselves from me more than usual. I couldn't put a finger on it. Nothing had changed on my part and I was always friendly to them at every turn. I had helped Anson recently with a few of his cases by lending out Reggie which he was thankful for but that was as far as it went.

Shale called for a regular Monday morning meeting to draw sheets from the skull. He started from a different side of the room from where I was sitting and made his way through the room several times stopping at each detective's desk to pull a sheet. There were a lot of tips this week and each detective pulled at least three sheets by the time Shale had finished.

After the skull was empty, Shale removed a piece of paper from his pocket handing it to me and requesting that I meet him in his office after the meeting to discuss the assignment he had given me.

He made a few administrative announcements to the squad before ushering us out of the room with his usual pronouncement, "All right, guys, let's get on the street. You can't buy dope sitting at your desks."

The detectives gathered up their backpacks and left the cave with their cold call assignments for the week.

I was flattered Shale now trusted me with special assignments and not just pulling random tips, many of which were small weed houses and houses that had already been abandoned just sitting empty.

I entered Shale's office as he was placing the skull on a shelf out of view. He was fumbling around with a few files before realizing I had entered the room and had seated myself.

The sheet of paper he had given me listed the address listed "1334 Paseo, #204." There were additional details mentioning cocaine was being sold at all times during the day and night from the apartment. The tip wasn't any more remarkable than any others I had received before.

Shale seemed uncomfortable and somewhat awkward addressing me and therefore kept the conversation short and brief, "Dewey, the chief asked us for a favor to get this apartment knocked down. Some city councilman's kid overdosed in there or something to that effect and the chief made a promise we would get to it."

"Yeah, not a problem, Tammy and I can knock this out tomorrow. Shouldn't be a problem, consider it done," I insisted.

"I'd like you to run Reggie in there on this one. This is a priority request and we need our best hitter at bat. This is Reggie's part of town and he's more likely to know someone in there than Tammy," Shale insisted.

I affirmed I would do as was needed and took my leave from Shale as I could tell he was preparing to make a phone call and was done discussing the subject with me.

As I walked towards the door, he quickly mentioned that he would have the raid team on the street tomorrow for Reggie on the Paseo cold call.

It wasn't unusual to get requests from the command staff from time to time. They attended citizen community meetings frequently where they often promised "the world" to the people in attendance.

No matter how big or small the issue was, the police commander who was put on the spot during the community meeting by an upset citizen vowed to put their best people and unlimited resources into correcting the problem that was brought to their attention for the "first time."

This particular nuisance house went far above the complaints of a citizen community meeting as a city councilman personally requested the assistance of SNU. Since the city council determined the budget of the police department, I now had a very important task at hand.

I understood why Shale had requested for Reggie to do the "cold call" at this location since failure in this endeavor was not an acceptable option.

Paseo Boulevard was one of the oldest boulevards in the city, dating back to 1893, which was home to some the wealthiest citizens of the city during that time. The boulevard was designed after the Paseo de La Reforma in Mexico City, a beautiful three mile boulevard between the Mexican capital and the castle of Chapultepec where rulers of Mexico had lived since the Spanish conquest.

The area was designed with large colorful flower beds, ornamental circles and fountains with statues. Paseo Boulevard in the northern section of the city was lined with red bricked apartment buildings constructed in a style from the time period of the early 1900s.

Sadly, some of the older buildings fell into disrepair by negligent landlords and were re-fashioned into low income family housing. The address we were given was in that category of a former once beautiful building now a low income apartment building frequented by addicts and transients.

I was excited to work with Reggie as I hadn't seen him for a few days. We kept in touch by phone in regard to the Paseo house. He assured me he could pull it off in his sleep and to put my anxieties to rest.

I met him at a parking lot about a quarter of a mile to the west of the location to get him his buy money and brief him on the apartment. He was already waiting for me in the Monte Carlo when I arrived and I could tell he had washed it recently. He was a huge fan of the glossy wheel shine products and it was evident he treated the tires of his car much like his shoes.

As I entered his car with him, I could see him looking at my feet as I sat down. I wondered what his reaction would be if I had walked through deep mud just before getting into his ride. We greeted with a handshake and I quickly apologized for the Chief's beating the Steelers 41-20. He gave a hearty laugh and apologized for the recent under performance of the Royals as well.

"I'm surprised you have time to watch any games with the amount of time you spend cleaning this car," I inquired.

"Shit, Dewey, this is nothing. Remember, I own a car wash and this is just my daily rinse off before I leave for the day to run my errands," he explained.

Reggie was a proprietor of a car wash on East Truman Road. It was a cash-only business where employees could be found easily as Reggie employed people who couldn't find jobs anywhere else. Most of his employees were guys with lengthy criminal records or substance abuse problems who ran the place for him while he was away.

Reggie often suggested his place would give a great discount to the department for their cruisers if they came in. Unfortunately, the department already had a contract with another car wash business, otherwise I have no doubt Reggie would have taken care of our cars with great detail, especially the wheels.

I handed Reggie forty dollars knowing he rarely spent that much but it was always better to have a little more if it was needed. I briefed him on the location and gave him as many details as I had regarding the apartment.

"I haven't been over there for a while, Dewey. I've seen smokers hanging around there a long time ago but I thought they closed that place down. Maybe it's opened back up," Reggie suggested.

I told Reggie I appreciated him helping us out with this place as the chief had personally requested it. Reggie again reminded me he would accomplish the task so well that I would in turn be rewarded with a promotion in rank when he had finished the undercover buy today. I laughed at his logic but appreciated his sincerity and wished him a safe trip as I exited his vehicle careful to not scuff any part of the interior.

Shale had the raid van parked to the East and tucked out of view within an apartment complex. He chose not to drive the van and was instead in an unmarked Ford Explorer. Shale positioned his vehicle further north of the location but had a good vantage point to see the foot traffic entering or leaving the front of the doors of the building. He broadcast over the radio that he was in position with an eye on the front door of the location.

I kept a visual tail of Reggie as he approached Paseo Boulevard from 11th Street and then made a southbound turn traveling two blocks towards the location. As he passed 12th Street I verified over the radio of his arrival. Shale affirmed in response that he had sight of "the Indian."

We always referred to an informant over the radio as "Indian" and a narc always was referenced as a "Charlie." After passing the eye to Shale, I turned west on 12th Street as not to follow Reggie too close to the address.

"All right, Indian is exiting his ride, walking towards the front doors and now he's out of my view," Shale detailed in his broadcast.

Reggie was relaxed as he had made these approaches on thousands of prior occasions working with SNU and sometimes working on his own with less supervision. His "cold-call" entrances into drug houses were now negotiated more through using his muscle memory of what had worked in the past rather than any type of difficult necessary improvisation others had to resort to.

He ascended the stairs to an open common area resembling a room more than a hallway with six apartment doors surrounding the landing he had reached. An apartment maintenance worker was sitting on ladder changing a fire alarm and didn't give Reggie much more than a glance as he entered the hallway.

Reggie dismissed the presence of any maintenance worker. In Reggie's experience he believed most of them gave little attention to the illicit activities that went on inside of apartments and were users themselves most of the time.

Reggie's task wold not be impeded by someone fixing fire alarms but the problem of actually finding apartment 204 would be an inconvenience for him as almost all of the doors were unnumbered. Upon closer inspection, two of the units' doors were not secured and they appeared unoccupied with missing locks and door knobs. Only one of the doors on the entire floor was denominated with an address which unfortunately was not the target location.

Reggie felt his odds were improving in locating the correct apartment as there were three doors to choose from. Even a random guess would present a 33% chance of picking the correct door. He decided to abstain from asking directions from the maintenance man until trying to resolve more of the puzzle out on his own. He took pride in trying to accomplish his assigned task without having to rely upon any outside assistance until absolutely needed. He believed he could listen carefully for any sounds of activity from behind the closed doors to help him find the correct address.

As the maintenance worker descended the ladder slowly, Reggie was inattentive or perhaps uninterested with the unusual lack of tools carried by the worker. Reggie was mentally immersed in the labyrinth maze of finding the correct door to knock on, ignoring the worker who held a hammer in his hand as he climbed down from the utility ladder.

Reggie felt confident for some reason to knock on the corner door furthest from the stairwell entry way. It was close to where the maintenance man was working on the fire alarm so maybe this was a telling indication of people inside of that unit.

It was a full hour before Shale suggested I check on Reggie. Reggie had not responded to three text messages and two phone calls during the hour. Shale directed the tactical squad to move the van within fifty yards of the front door in the event there was a problem. Shale also parked directly behind the van closing the distance needed to quickly enter the structure if needed.

I could tell from the amount of the blood on Reggie's body and the spray pattern against the wall, Reggie had been killed quickly and with the claw side of a hammer which was now lying next to his body. Pancho had used enough strength in his strikes to crush the top back portion of Reggie's skull, completely piercing it and exposing the interior similar to a ruptured egg shell. Reggie's treasured Pittsburgh cap was found several feet from his body which made the scene even more personally horrifying.

The entire building was locked down and became a crime scene. The landlord arrived and was very cooperative allowing the tactical team permission to search all of the unoccupied units which was the majority of the building. He was in the process of refurbishing the structure and only five of the twelve units contained occupants, most of whom gave consent to search their apartments.

The occupant of the unit Reggie had intended to knock on was an elderly woman who was unaware the homicide had even occurred until she was contacted in regard to the dead body lying in front of her door. She did however give a limited description of a maintenance man working on the fire alarm in front of her door. She stated she had even thanked the kind gentlemen for fixing the alarm and asked him to make it "very loud" for her as she was diminished in hearing.

We all knew the answer before even having to ask the landlord, a maintenance worker had not been scheduled to perform any work inside of the building on that day.

In the days to follow, I made a nuisance of myself with the assigned homicide detective, David Carrier. I was fortunate, as David had been in the unit for three years and was clearing an unusually higher percentage of his cases than the average. I think his success was fostered by the fact he was single without kids and given that he spent literally every minute of each day thinking about his cases and trying to resolve them. I don't know how he did it. He loved and lived his job 24-7 and had no personal life to speak of.

This homicide was unusual to him. David told me his loyalty was always to the victim and the victim's family where he was obligated to present his beliefs and evidence without guesswork supported with compelling evidence in whatever direction it took the case. He stated confidently without hesitation this homicide was a targeted crime. Reggie's death was not a case of being in the wrong place at the wrong time but was the opposite. He was led specifically to the location of his murder.

The ladder under the fire alarm was simply a ruse. The fire alarm was rusted and partially painted over for at least a decade. The alarm was absent of any tool marks showing someone was legitimately attempting to fix or replace the antiquated broken device.

I helped provide David with a detailed background of Reggie to build a profile of any person who would want to harm him. The problem with any scenario, no matter how antagonistic a potential past relationship that Reggie may have had, was that the location and time of Reggie's arrival was known to the killer. This person had the knowledge Reggie would be inside of 1334 Paseo Boulevard on the day of his murder and also knew he would be on the second floor.

David and I had internal thoughts starting to develop that we each hoped the other would mention first as a way to break the unusual ice that covered the next possibility.

"I think it's somewhat strange from how you told me the operation was conducted that no one observed anyone leave through the front door," David mentioned breaking the ice as I had hoped he would.

David and I met at 1334 Paseo together to re-examine the exterior points of surveillance that covered any entry into the structure. We walked up the exterior fire exit staircase on the rear of the building that was not facing Paseo Boulevard and was not visible from Shale's vantage point. Each door needed a key for entry and the locks were painted over. It was possible the doors could have been used as exit points by the murderer but not as an entry point as the keyholes were painted over.

The building was surrounded by empty lots to the North and south. Any person who exited the fire escape would still need to leave the area on foot or by vehicle from the side of the building facing away from the Boulevard. Shale would have been able to see a person walking or driving away in the alley behind the structure with little difficulty. David and I even went so far as to re-enact the surveillance point of where Shale's car was sitting. I took Shale's position and David attempted to leave the area in his vehicle parked behind the structure which was immediately visible. He was even more easy to spot walking on foot through the alleyway.

There was the possibility Shale had glanced at his watch, looked away for a moment, missing the killer's exit, but if you knew Shale, this was probably not the case.

David and I reached the same conclusion without speaking it aloud to each other. If Shale was maintaining his surveillance of the building, he would've have observed Reggie's murderer leaving the building either on foot or by vehicle whether the person exited the front door or through the fire escape stairway on the rear side of the building.

Shale made the admission to David from the onset of the investigation that no one was seen leaving or entering the building except for Reggie. The murder of Reggie had literally occurred with police officers watching the location of the homicide at the exact time the crime was being committed. David knew this scenario was improbable at best.

I was still in shock over the events and the anger had not yet set in. My concerns of solving the crime were eased as I could tell David was intensely intrigued by this case almost as much as I was. From his personality, I knew he would obsess about this case relentlessly, most likely visiting the crime scene location repeatedly, even if it was on his day off. He would engross his thoughts over any little detail to point him in a direction to find Reggie's killer.

The shock had dissipated and I came to accept the idea Reggie was now gone and he had perished under my supervision. He had survived thousands of drug houses before me, working with many other detectives, including Skinner who probably sent him to much more dangerous places than I had.

I repeatedly questioned myself if I had overlooked something in our preparation. I read the tip sheet continually for any clue or red flag that signaled some type of hidden danger I should have seen before sending Reggie inside.

The mechanics of the operation itself further pushed my thoughts back to accusations of Shale's possible involvement. I had to make my conclusions as objective as possible regardless of my opinions of the man. I created a list in my mind of things that needed to be explained away or crossed off the list to move past Shale as a suspect.

Foremost on the list was the fact Shale hand-picked the location and disseminated the assignment to not me, but to Reggie. He specifically requested Reggie enter the Paseo building and had more or less created the time frame of when Reggie would arrive at the location. And finally, Shale put himself as the gatekeeper of surveillance as the only person who would see the killer leave the location.

As soon as I had convinced myself of a nefarious conspiracy involving Shale I equally unconvinced myself that a decorated career police officer would do something like this. The only reason my mind could find for a man like Shale to kill another person was out of self preservation from a threat Reggie posed. Shale wasn't being threatened by Reggie so it had to be a fluke. It had to fall into a one in a million chance category of unlucky stars aligning that Reggie had walked into some ambush. Maybe he had been mistaken for someone else.

I drove downtown to meet Randy in the basement equipment vault of headquarters before meeting with Tammy later in the morning. The rat phone was being changed out for something newer and more reliable. I was glad as it was obnoxiously big and bright yellow and I hoped Randy would have something that more closely resembled a real phone. It seemed in my mind that if the rat phone ever fell from my pocket, someone would immediately recognize it as an undercover listening post and not a real cell phone.

Randy was already standing at the counter when I arrived. As was customary, his cane was at arm's length nearby but he relied upon the ledge of the counter to assist him when he was administering property to police personnel. He seemed less jovial upon my arrival and more concerned of my appearance.

I had lost over twenty pounds since I had first seen him when Country introduced us. I was now ensconced in an overgrown mane of a beard and my hair was a tangled tuft of a mess. My face showed the effects of anxiety eating away at my body and sleep deprivation. I knew I was unsightly and unhealthy to look at.

"Dewey, here's your phone, son. You just need to sign for it. You look like you've seen a thing or two out there on the street. How's everything at SNU?" he asked, genuinely concerned as to what my response would be.

Randy was the wisest soul I knew and he could instinctively tell by my response I was in a strange place at the moment, "Thanks for the phone, Randy. You ever have those days when you feel like you can't tell the good guys from the bad, you don't know who you can really trust?"

He was quick to respond and I was thankful he didn't ask for additional clarification, "I do. Believe me, I do. But you need to remember, there's no gray area between right and wrong. John 3:20, everyone who does evil hates the light, and will not come into the light for fear that their deeds will be exposed. Maybe you need to shine some light on your problems."

I thanked him for the new phone, his advice and took a sheet of paper he offered me with simplified instructions created for cops on how to operate the new rat phone. We exchanged a parting look in which I took him to understand somehow he knew that I was headed for a storm of some sort.

I left downtown and started towards Tammy's place. I was literally too mentally unfocused to decipher what Randy had recited but I wrote down his Bible passage on a note pad to read at a later time with his parting advice to "shine some light on my problems." I knew whatever he told me was something important I would need to guide me or possibly keep me from harm's way at a later time.

As Tammy left her apartment and walked to the Jeep, I could tell she was upset over the death of Reggie. I had called her immediately after the murder to make sure she had heard the news from me and not on the street from someone else. She had known Reggie as well from the street.

and like almost everyone he met, she was a friend to him. They had even worked a couple of cases together for Tyra's unit back in the day. We made our usual stop at the store before discussing anything related to work. Tammy raised an eyebrow as I handed her a twenty instead of her normal ten, "Tammy, I could use a beer if you don't mind grabbing me one too."

Tammy returned from the QuikTrip with her armful of "work" groceries for the morning including my large 22 ounce beverage. I noticed two uniformed officers in their cruiser giving Tammy and myself the once over look as potential targets to stop. I could tell they were waiting for us to leave first so they could pull us over so we simply sat long enough for them to become disinterested or perhaps dispatched to a call.

I told Tammy everything that had been on my mind with Reggie's death and my suspicions towards Shale. Tammy wasn't really fond of Shale even before hearing my concerns of his involvement and I knew she would be an impartial jury to weigh the evidence I presented to her.

I gave her the details of what David and I learned from examining the crime scene carefully. I presented everything to her as objectively and impartially as possible as I wanted her honest opinion either way. I even presented the possibility of Reggie simply being mistaken for somebody else at the apartment.

She remained attentive and asked questions from time to time during my presentation which was a good sign to me as she was searching for a decision of her own. We were both smoking her cherry Black and Mild cigars now as we held court for Shale in the Laredo. I occasionally alchemized my palette alternating between my daily Marlboro cigarettes to her flavored cigars.

"Dewey, that son of a bitch is a murderer, plain and simple," she finally concluded after deliberation.

I told her I was relieved by her decision as I was continuously questioning the sanity of my suspicions. "Tammy, I believe he did this or at least let it happen but why would he do this? What the hell could the reason be? There's no sense to this," I declared.

She suggested a simple idea that connected the dots, broke the fog away from the mystery of what had happened and left me speechless at the acuity of her wisdom.

"Dewey, Reggie died from a situation that connected him to Shale that we don't know about yet," she plausibly suggested.

It hit me like cold water and I was a little embarrassed I hadn't put it together on my own without Tammy's trigger. "But I do know what's connecting them, Tammy,"

I pulled the Jeep into a parking lot to stop and think. I closed my eyes and played the entire memory in my head of initially presenting Reggie's information to Shale. I could see Shale's distressed face as I mentioned the names, Antonio and Desean. The only bridge between Shale and Reggie was the information I had passed between them. I had unwittingly caused Reggie's death by exposing Shale's criminal associates.

Shale had asked me for Reggie's file to learn where he lived. He needed Reggie's address to set up a fabricated cold call in Reggie's neighborhood baiting Reggie instead of Tammy to enter the trap.

Shale was on the take, a crooked cop stealing apples from the cart. He was involved with a crew moving millions of dollars worth of heroin and cocaine. By Shale's admission, from his own mouth, he didn't care about the lives and safety of informants. They were a tool in the tool box and had no other purpose. Shale had snuffed out Reggie without losing a minute of sleep over the decision. He didn't hold the hammer that killed Reggie but he had put it in someone else's hands to do it.

"What are we going to do, Dewey?" Tammy asked.

I suggested to her we needed to be very careful not to bring up the names Antonio and Desean around Shale. Shale would be watching and listening to see if I started investigating them again. I could find myself in the same situation as Reggie if I put Shale into a corner again. As far as Shale knew, I had lost my investigative leads with the passing of Reggie.

"He's got other cops helping him," Tammy claimed with confidence.

I agreed. There had to be other people filling their pockets working with Shale. We had to assume there were other people inside of SNU who were aligned with him stealing money and drugs.

I suggested to Tammy that we could both use a mental health day to which she agreed. It was not a good idea to go inside of any more houses until we had our heads on straighter and were focused. I dropped Tammy at home and told her I would come up with something tomorrow.

As she exited the Jeep she exhaled her cigar and cautiously advised, "Be careful, Dewey." Through all of the adventures together, this was the first time she had said this to me.

CHAPTER 13 - MENTAL DESCENT

I was now alone at SNU. I didn't know how far Shale's reach was throughout the police department. It would logistically be difficult for him to be working alongside significant drug traffickers if he couldn't trust someone to have his back on the streets. He had to be working with other cops, specifically people within his own crew of narcs.

If I approached the wrong person at SNU, one of Shale's people, I would inadvertently position myself as an adversary without knowing it. I would have no way of knowing if Shale decided to prepare a "hot" house for me as he did for Reggie.

I pulled into the garage at the cave and started to gather my equipment before going inside when I saw Alice standing at the passenger side door of the Jeep. I rolled down the window to greet her, "Hey Alice, are you done for the day?"

She looked around cautiously as if deciding if it was safe enough to speak to me out of the normal context of casual conversation, "Can I talk with you alone for a minute?"

I pushed open the door of the Jeep and invited her to sit inside, "Welcome to my office, pardon the mess."

She would be the first to admonish me with humor about the dirty conditions of my vehicle but instead she was stoic in her disposition to discuss something important on her mind.

"Thank you, something's not right with what happened to Reggie and I know you feel it, too," she confided.

There was the possibility Alice was a confederate as well. She had prepared the tip sheets for Shale and had worked for him for years. She could've been responsible for preparing the location of Reggie's murder under the direction of Shale. I was careful not to play my hand and display my suspicions of Shale to her in the event he had sent her to figure out my next move.

"I prepare all of the tips that are called, mailed or brought in. I de-conflict and cross check the address in a central database to prevent other agencies from targeting the same locations. This also is a measure for officer safety to prevent two different undercover operations from occurring in the same place. I check everything that comes through the door, Jeff. This is the first time in all my six years working for SNU and out of thousands of tips, Ryan prepared his own tip sheet," she informed me.

Alice had now mentioned Shale's name first under the shadow of suspicion which was a good sign she was not being sent by him to see where I stood. I still remained careful to not divulge I already knew he was a murderer.

"I think he purposely hid this from me and I don't think this came from the chief as he said it did. Ryan is always adamant about cross checking locations. He doesn't like the idea of some other crew taking a stat from us. If this had actually come from the Chief of Police, I would have been told to take an ad out in the newspaper announcing this was our spot," she exaggerated to make her point. "I checked, he didn't deconflict or cross check the Paseo apartment to make sure another crew wasn't working in that area. I know I sound crazy, but it's almost like he had that place picked out just for Reggie and knew something bad was going to happen there," she solemnly suggested.

I knew she was not sent by Shale at this point in our conversation as she was throwing too much dirt on him to include providing a paper evidence trail implicating him in the murder.

"We need to be careful with what we say around this place, Alice," I advised. "Have you told this to anyone else?" I asked.

Alice confided she didn't trust a couple of the other narcs and had only decided to approach me as she had always trusted Country. I asked Alice to keep our conversation confidential until I could present more evidence of Shale's criminal conspiracy. She agreed and was relieved I was receptive to her suspicions and shared similar concerns. I did not discuss with her the motive of Reggie's death which was Shale erasing the link between himself and his drug dealing associates.

"Alice, do you think there's anyone else here at SNU that we should be careful around, maybe helping Shale?" I asked.

"The only thing I know is Anson got in trouble, big trouble a few years ago for drugs and Ryan helped cover it up or made it go away somehow," she divulged.

Alice didn't provide additional details of how she knew of Anson's problems and I didn't press her for any more information. Alice exited the Jeep and again was still guarded to see if anyone had seen her talking to me. We agreed to keep in contact with each other going forward sharing any new information.

I gathered my radio and slipped it into a side pocket of my pack before leaving the Jeep. I made my way inside and sat at my desk to work on a few reports. The room was quiet with a few phone calls in progress with the people who were there with me.

Shale was sitting in a chair with his back to me talking to Anson.

They were preoccupied in their conversation and were unaware I had entered the room. I stared intently at them as if I could somehow discern clues from watching them converse. I knew they were nothing more than criminals who hadn't been caught.

I could feel my anger stirring as I caught foggy images in my mind, seeing Reggie's contorted face as when I had found him lying in the hallway. Whenever I saw a deceased person, I always tried to avoid looking at their faces, if possible. The face is personal. It's an autograph of someone's life, their personality, their emotions and sometimes their thoughts.

The victims of homicides were more palatable if you only saw a pair of their feet exposed from underneath a plastic crime scene tarp. If you couldn't see the signs of a struggle or fear in their face, it evaporated from your memories quicker.

Even if you were an acquaintance of deceased person, if you saw their face in death, it was, in my opinion, an intrusion of their privacy. It wasn't meant for someone to see, a person's most private and desperate struggle of life on display for someone else to view and to judge. I had made the mistake of looking at Reggie's face when I found him and now it was impossibly difficult to dilute the memory of his pain and suffering.

There were no more doubts in my mind of the events leading to Reggie's death. I knew I was looking at Reggie's murderer who would kill anyone else who threatened to expose him, including Tammy and myself.

I was clear-eyed and astute enough to realize Shale was a smarter and more experienced cop than I. He would read me and quickly determine I suspected him of the crime. He was patiently waiting for me to give him the reason to hand me an address where some person waited behind a door ready beat me to death with a hammer.

In my mental calculations, I reasonably believed my sentencing would end up in the ballpark of 16 to 20 years for killing Shale if I took a plea to second degree murder and could articulate my fears well enough to the assigned judge of my case.

I physically checked my holster for my Glock underneath my clothes even though I knew it was still there. People on the street who carried concealed firearms were sometimes easy to spot in this manner as they repeatedly and nervously checked for the presence of their own firearm under their clothing. It was silly that I was doing this as well. It was the mental preparation of killing Shale in the middle of the SNU office which gave me the nervous inclination to verify my weapon was still on my person.

I decided to employ the popular technique of "hiding in plain sight" to approach Shale and fire a single round into the base of his head where the skull jointed the spinal column. My approach would be a routine path of travel for me as Anson's desk was next to the hallway that exited from the room we were in. It would more likely appear to Anson I was leaving the room rather than approaching his desk as I seldom spoke with him.

If I threw my weapon down fast enough and placed my hands into the air as a sign of surrender, there was a possibility Anson might not return fire if I was visibly disarmed after killing Shale. Unfortunately, the chances were falling more towards the realistic scenario of Anson returning fire as Shale's head would invariably explode with pieces of his skull and brain matter striking Anson. I would not fault him for this, as it would be justified on his part.

I threw my calculated prison sentence range out of the window now, as killing Anson and Shale together would most likely elicit conversations of the lethal injection for a high profile double capital murder case. It was a balanced decision weighed with the assured safety of my family, Tammy, Alice and any other person who came to the same knowledge I possessed.

I reflected on my father's advice of giving everything you do in life 100% effort and presumed it was applicable with killing corrupt police officers in the middle of the office on Tuesday as well.

I stood up and placed my left hand near my waistline in preparation for lifting the material of my shirt high enough to reach the grip of my firearm with my other hand unobstructed. The entire rehearsed procedure of clearing a garment to fire from concealment usually took well under two-seconds to complete with an accurate shot placement afterwards. I had time on my side and wouldn't need to accelerate the process.

"You're too skinny, crackhead, you want a cookie?" Netta asked me with a huge smile, showing stains of chocolate across her teeth.

She stood in my path to Shale holding a large cookie in her hand for me to take. Her appearance was more refined than normal with her dark spiky hair combed differently with some of it now covering more of her forehead than before. Her large brown eyes seemed childlike as she held a cookie that was much larger than her hand. Netta had taken pride in making cookies for the first time and it was evident she didn't have the greatest culinary skills.

My mouth was so dry I could not speak clearly. Shale was looking over his shoulder at Netta and myself. I had been in a fantasy world of my own creation and my premeditations now seemed maniacally irrational as if made by someone else. I wondered if I was in an early stage of mental illness and if I would regress further with additional provocation.

Netta laughed as she slowly touched the cookie to my lips, "Does Dewey want a cookie?"

I slowly took the cookie from her and thanked her in an odd quiet voice while looking past her towards Anson and Shale. Their conversation was over with Shale walking out of the room towards his office.

I quickly diminished from a dangerous Sicario to a gaunt, lanky dirty man holding a leviathan of a poorly made cookie.

I gathered my backpack and left the cave. It was difficult to sit at my desk knowing Shale was in the same building separated by only a wall between the narcs bullpen and his office.

I took the Jeep for a lengthy ride throughout the city as my mind searched for any possible alternatives to waiting for Shale to eventually kill me when he determined the time was right. I parked the Jeep and tried to eat Netta's cookie as my stomach churned. I realized I had not eaten for two days from the nauseating mental stress I was digesting.

I visualized my problems dissolving immediately with a small inhalation of crack that would also help Netta's cookie taste a little better. I found myself reminiscing of my time with Peanut and Myra and how enjoyable the experience of smoking was despite the other horrific events of that day.

I course corrected my thoughts once again, realizing smoking crack along with planning to kill Shale was cowardice. It was mental escapism of a small child who couldn't change the dinner menu from asparagus to chicken nuggets shaped like dinosaurs. I needed to grow the fuck up and deal with the situation at hand, finding a solution.

I had written Randy's bible verse in a notebook which I now carried with me and decided to read aloud. The verse had sounded better written in my notebook than repeated it in my head or spoken. I had hoped some revelation would come from the heavens afterwards repeating the verse several times. I took the message to mean I needed some bright light to expose on the crooked cops who surrounded me but I couldn't identify. I put away the notebook in my pack and decided to call it a night, returning home.

As I pulled into the driveway, my cell rang with a call from David. I contemplated letting it go to voicemail and calling him in the morning but decided to see if he had any new information. It was probably urgent as he was calling later than usual but I reminded myself he was on his phone at all hours of the night working his homicide cases.

We greeted briefly before he asked if I was available to meet some people in the morning who had leads on the case.

"I don't want to get into details now, Jeff and believe me, it's better if you just come with me on this one and trust me," he advised.

He swore me to keeping the appointment and to absolutely not mention it to anyone at SNU. He provided me with address of the United States Attorney's Office for the Western District of Missouri located in downtown Kansas City, Missouri on 9th Street.

I didn't have the energy to spend thinking of what the meeting was about and decided to focus on getting at least six hours of sleep uninterrupted before facing the next day.

Red arrived to his restaurant in Blue Springs around eight in the morning to oversee the arrival of recently purchased kitchen equipment. Red trusted his manager who insisted the equipment was a necessary investment with the amount of new business coming in and the recent expansion of their menu. The acquired $40,000 worth of equipment was far less than the exuberant costs of one of Red's trips across the globe to acquire a new tattoo but he still felt obligated to inspect the items being unloaded off the truck.

Red's cooks arrived to the restaurant at three in the morning each day to start the hickory wood fires for the slow cooking of meats to be ready for the day. The doors of Red's restaurant were opened precisely at eleven each day without fail, usually to a small line of people waiting in the parking lot.

Red meticulously checked each piece of equipment as if a part could be missing or damaged in transit to his restaurant. Red occasionally glanced at his watch as he knew he had a business meeting at nine with Shale.

Red was behind the restaurant in an enclosed lot containing several large outdoor pit cookers and a few tables for outside dining. Red's employees were too busy to notice any visitors who Red met with when he was behind the restaurant.

Regardless of the purpose of Red's meeting, whether to negotiate the price of heroin with a customer or conducting a more legitimate business transaction, Red preferred the back lot of his restaurant to talk to people. Red preferred to be in familiar surroundings with people he knew and he refused to sit in cars with people to do any type of business.

Shale arrived a few minutes early and entered the back lot through a side gate. Red was always cordial with Shale but they never shook hands as if the gesture was inappropriate for their type of association. Perhaps, they feared some surveillance team would see the handshake between then and assume it was part of a nefarious drug transaction.

Their conversations were always private but direct to the point without the use of talking in coded references to conceal the true nature of their business dealings. They were big boys and masters of their universes and trying to camouflage their conversations with silly codes was a sign of weakness.

Red had asked for the meeting with Shale to receive of any updates into the investigation of Reggie's murder.

"There hasn't been any changes as far as I know. It's an open and shut situation, especially without a witness," explained Shale.

"Is it really open and shut?" asked Red.

Shale seemed puzzled at the question, "I'm not sure what you mean."

"There's still a witness around boss. The new kid who was running Reggie around. He knows about Desean and he knows about me. Maybe he's figured out why Reggie's gone and that was the reason," Red suggested without insinuating anything further.

"I've got a close eye on him. He can't make any moves without us knowing about it and regardless of what he believes, Reggie was his only source to getting anywhere. He's back working dime bags and crack houses, nothing else. If he starts to ask questions again, we'll address the situation as needed," Shale explained.

"Can you recruit this kid? Get his hands dirty so we know there's not going to be a problem down the road," Red suggested.

"Nah, the kid's a total square, not much dirt under his nails," Shale described unflatteringly of myself. "If he gets caught doing something crazy, then yeah, maybe, but it's always a risk."

Red's legitimate intention for the meeting was to gauge Shale's receptiveness to addressing a fellow police officer in the same manner as an informant who was a problem for everyone. It took some time, but Shale finally picked up on the underlying question on Red's mind. Shale was careful, neither committing nor rejecting the idea outright.

"Red, let's not get our corsets in a bunch over this kid until he makes a move. He can barely make a ham sandwich without burning down the kitchen. Trust me, we need to be patient on this one. In a few months, he'll back in a patrol car pulling over drunks and hooking up Saturday night wife-beaters and you'll see that I'm right," Shale smugly assured Red.

"I'm not worried cause I know we're partners and partners look after each other, and you'll let me know if this kid changes course," Red cautiously advised.

Shale seemed to focus more on watching the meat cook on the grill in front of Red than taking in his message, "Red, listen to me on this, wrap your burnt ends in peach butcher paper instead of foil. The paper lets out the steam and you get a better char on the top of that meat. Trust me Red, peach paper."

CHAPTER 14 - THE FEDS

I met David fifteen minutes before our meeting was scheduled to begin. He was dressed in his normal business casual attire of a clean collared shirt and pleated pants. He had thrown a sport coat on over his shirt. I was dressed in my usual Dewey the crack-head attire but took care to fasten few more buttons than usual of my outer work shirt to dress up a little bit for the occasion. I also finger combed some leftover particles of food and cigar tobacco fibers from my beard as it was probably going to be a meeting with notable important people in attendance and first impressions are everything in life.

We provided our credentials to enter the federal building and get past the security station. We were taken to a small side room to lock up our weapons in lockers before entering the large building. I had never been inside of a federal US Attorney's office but it was evident there had been no expense spared in the construction of the facility.

We made our way to the 14th floor with little conversation inside of the elevator. It didn't seem important at this time to ask for details regarding the meeting as I would know the purpose of the meeting in a matter of a few minutes.

As we entered the room it was already full of people. It was evident the meeting was purposely started much sooner than our expected arrival as everyone was already viewing reports in front of them and a power-point presentation had been started which was displayed on an enormous screen on the wall.

I could tell the room was filled with an assortment of FEDs: agents, task force officers, intelligence analysts and federal prosecutors. My eyes quickly spotted a familiar face in the crowd at the end of the table who stood out amongst the others. Netta was smiling with a weird Cheshire cat-like grin upon seeing me enter the room.

The room became very quiet and all eyes looked at me in odd interest of my gaunt dirty appearance. David and I found two empty chairs where we sat ourselves at the table of the "important people."

A robust man with silver thinning hair and an expensively tailored suit immediately greeted me us as we sat ourselves at the table, "Detectives Moore and Carrier, thank you for coming in today. My name is Dan Galen, I'm a federal prosecutor with the US Attorney's Office, Public Corruption Unit. My co-prosecutor is Julie Hutting to my right. Let me quickly introduce everyone here on the Task Force before we get started, FBI agents, Adam Richetti, Mark Agnello, Brandon Clark, Dylan West and Lisa Knoll.

We also have DEA agents, Derek Foster, Jason Donovan, Brian Mackay and Roland Pacheco. We have two Jackson County Sheriff Deputies, David Jurado and Emery Van Laere. We have three intelligence analysts, Debra Waters, Jennifer Kane and Sharon Kaplin assisting us too. I think you're already familiar with fellow Detective Netta Quintero and Sergeant Tyra Benedict with the Kansas City Drug Unit."

Netta grinned and gave a small wave from the end of the table, "Surprise, Dewey!"

The room's tension from the stuffy collection of FEDs was immediately broken with laughter from hearing my street name "Dewey" spoken aloud.

I was surprised as I had not seen Tyra sitting at the table until she was introduced by Dan. She was hard to read and didn't say anything during the meeting. She simply looked at me with contempt like I was a part of the rat's nest she considered SNU to be.

"You're at the table today from Netta vouching for your character," explained Dan. "We live in a world where it's hard to know who to trust sometimes."

I took a moment during Dan's pause to greet the room, "Hey, guys."

Dan returned to his introductions, "Let's get started as we have a lot to cover today. We started this task force almost four years ago from information received as a result of a DEA investigation. The DEA was investigating a large scale Kansas City heroin trafficker named Antonio Hill. We were up on multiple phone lines for him and his organization when we began hearing intercepted calls with guys who sounded more like cops than your average every-day drug dealers. It took a bit of manpower but we in fact identified them as cops to include your supervisor Ryan Shale.

Ryan and his fellow co-conspirators have been stealing evidence in the form of drugs and money for the last five years from other traffickers on the streets. The drugs are given to Antonio to be sold again with the profits shared between them. On the streets, Ryan and his crew are referred to as the Super Friends."

FBI agent Clark interjected, "The case stalled for a year with the guys dropping phones constantly and informants disappearing off the radar. We got a break when Netta approached Sgt. Benedict with her concerns over what she was seeing inside of SNU. Sgt. Benedict and Netta came to visit us and blew the lid off these guys."

Netta told us about Ryan recruiting people for his squad to help him steal money and drugs. We arranged for Netta to "fail" a random drug test which baited Shale into recruiting her into his inner crew of confederates. It worked and we had the perfect informant inside of Shale's squad. We waited a few months before deciding to bring you into the tent with everyone when Netta said you were good people."

"I seriously hope this period of waiting the fuck around until the right moment didn't include allowing Reggie to be beaten to death with a hammer," I angrily explained without filtering my emotions.

The room suddenly got heavier as people realized I was shifting culpability of Reggie's death to anyone in the room who knew it was going to happen.

"Jeff, if anyone sat by and let this happen, they would be included in our grand jury of the already sixteen defendants I'm getting ready to show you. I can promise you, no one here in this room, to my knowledge, knew that was going to happen, and, if I find out the contrary, that person will be facing a twenty year federal indictment. You have my word on that, Jeff," Dan assured me.

I felt the anger leaving my flushed face and hoped I could trust Galen with his assurances. Dan began a slide presentation of the case which began with all of the defendant photos to include Ryan Shale, Ernie Infante-Duran, Anson Kane, Charlie Lawson, Dan Hirst, Antonio Hill and Desean Hill. There was another cop in the defendant line-up who worked for the Independence Missouri Police department in the city to the east of Kansas City. The remaining other eight co-defendants included non-law enforcement bad guys who worked with Antonio. Some of the people were from Arizona who supplied Antonio with his drugs.

The federal corruption case was worked off the radar of the police department without anyone being aware of the investigation aside from Tyra and Netta. The police chief was kept in the dark in regard to the den of thieves in his own house.

Chief Bryan McColley was going to be briefed 24 hours before the multi agency take-down was scheduled to occur in two weeks. Chief McColley would be allowed to present himself to the press and city council as a leader within the federal task force in a push to clean up his own agency. It was politically a ground ball he was being served. It was unfair in my mind as if we were giving the captain of the Titanic accolades and praise for only hitting one iceberg instead of two.

Arresting cops is a slightly different animal than arresting regular bad guys. The idea of law enforcement personnel losing careers, their families, their pensions and being incarcerated with other criminals leads to a lot of unpredictable reactions ranging from on the spot suicides to people fleeing from prosecution.

Two separate tactical FBI take-down units were being flown in from across the country to participate in the arrest operation. One of the FBI units en route to Kansas City was referenced by the operation name, Boxcar. They were the tip-of-the-spear type of guys who were used for breaching hijacked airplanes and other high risk operations. Most of Boxcar guys had military backgrounds with about half coming from Special Forces in their prior military service. I guess when the Boxcar dudes came around it was not a good day for some people.

The impressive presentation went on for two hours elaborately describing the roles and illegal crimes committed by each participant. There were connections to other criminal groups of people outside of Missouri who distributed hundreds of pounds of heroin and cocaine throughout the United States. It was truly an impressive little group of bad guys.

I felt like the guy in the restaurant for his birthday dinner wondering if someone at the table had secretly told the waiter. Would the staff arrive singing with a piece of cake or was it simply over after the meal was finished? I could tell the meal was coming to an end but my piece of birthday cake was on the way to the table.

When the slideshow ended, Dan took a break to drink some water. "Sharon can you put up the slide of our the last guy?" he asked.

The last slide was a single surveillance photo taken 100 yards from a subject with as much clarity as a Bigfoot photo taken with a Polaroid camera in the 80's.

"We don't know much about this guy other than he just kills people. He doesn't talk on the phone and is very surveillance aware of his surroundings. He's been a ghost to follow. He uses the name Pancho and works for Antonio at the moment. We believe he's a military guy or maybe has law enforcement experience.

We pulled his prints from a glass door pushed open with the palm of his hand in Crown Center downtown. His prints aren't on file, so he's not been arrested domestically as far was we can tell.

David has done a great job and matched Pancho's prints to fingerprints pulled from the inside of a taxi cab of a homicide victim. A cab driver was killed with two other guys inside of a dope house run by Ramon Harris who was also one of the victims. We believe Ramon at one point worked for Antonio. The cab driver's car was abandoned a couple miles from the scene.

We suspect this guy Pancho took the cab driver's car after killing everyone inside of Ramon's place. And for the last puzzle piece of good news, I'll let David deliver it," Dan conceded.

"Good news, Jeff, we pulled a partial matching print from the ladder inside the Paseo apartments. This Pancho guy killed Reggie. We got him," David excitedly pronounced to the task force.

"Well, let's go get this guy. What's the holdup on arresting him? Or am I not going to like the answer?" I asked with uncertainty.

"I'm not going to blow smoke. It's a very weak circumstantial case at best. There were other prints pulled from the taxi cab and nothing was found in Ramon's place to put Pancho there. The prints on the ladder are helpful but nothing was found on the hammer.

We've got some ideas, but I want to say to you first, you've been through a lot of crap and no one in this room is going to fault you if you say no," Dan explained sincerely.

Dan's co-prosecutor, Julie interjected, "The other option, if everyone here in the room is in agreement and wants to roll the dice, I'll support putting Pancho on the Grand Jury indictment with the other defendants. But, if we're going to be honest responsible adults in the room, we know we'll lose the case. It will be an embarrassing setback and the judge will keep it in the back of his mind with the other defendant's cases. Antonio is not going to testify against Pancho as he will then share culpability for the four murders."

"Nope, I'm not giving this the five dollar effort with this guy so he gets a pass and kills more people, maybe a cop. I don't care, put me down for whatever plan you guys have, the crazier the better," I volunteered without hesitation.

DEA Agent Foster was the first to break the ice of the difficult ask on behalf of everyone in the room, "Is it possible to repeat what happened to Reggie in some form or another to put Antonio and Shale into such a tight corner they pull Pancho out on the street again?"

I took a minute to weigh in my mind the real possibility of accomplishing this without Shale figuring it was a ruse on my part, "I don't have a problem with being the bait for Pancho but Shale is a smart guy. He knows I already suspect him of setting up Reggie. He'll immediately know this is some type of set-up, if I bring up Antonio. It would have to come from someone else's mouth to his ears that he needed to act fast before I made a move on something I knew about. Maybe—"

"I'll handle that part, Dewey," interrupted Netta.

"I wish you would just call me Jeff in front of my new friends here, Netta," I embarrassingly chuckled.

Netta was right. She had the brass tacks to pull it off. She had worked undercover for the FBI and DEA as a corrupt undercover narc infiltrating Shale's squad from the inside of its rotten core. She alone had caused the fall of the narcs. It was her, one person and no one else. She was now mythology, legend and lore far above the exploits of Scott Skinner on any of his best days. I had seen it in her eyes, she was a true believer in her cause and lived without fear. This five foot hundred pound Latina was the most dangerous person in the room. She had memorialized the Super Friend's sins from inside the quiet houses sealing everyone's fate to years of prison time.

It would be challenging for Netta to convince Shale he needed to kill Tammy and myself but I believed she could do it. For Shale and Antonio, killing an informant was like throwing out old tennis shoes that were green from mowing the lawn in them. I'm sure they had caused the deaths of other problem informants in the past by simply putting the informants identities on the streets for others to handle the task of disposing of them.

Killing a cop is a harder pill to swallow even for Shale and Antonio. Dead cops get folded flags, parades, promises of justice to their killers and in Missouri, death penalties are handed out to cop killers.

Maybe Shale had blurred and distorted the lines of morality in his mind so far he was now able to get to this point out of self preservation. He had no doubt put people undeservingly in prison and the grave, not to speak of the millions of dollars he stole from other criminals. He would assuredly be the subject of accountable retribution if he found himself in an armored bus heading towards Jefferson City.

I remembered a conversation, one of many with Chuck cautioning me to always respect the man on the street who has nothing to lose. He is the one to fear. Shale was the man who had nothing to lose by killing myself or Tammy. He was dead without his badge protecting him from the people on the streets he had wronged. By Tammy and I taking away his badge, it was the same as killing him.

Randy's shared verse, John 3:20, "Everyone who does evil hates the light, and will not come into the light for fear that their deeds will be exposed" was no longer a mystery to me. I understood its meaning and I felt it now giving me purpose. I wasn't talented like Skinner or as brave as Netta but I now had this light as my weapon. I just needed to get Shale to step into the light and it would be over for him regardless of what happened to me.

I left the task force meeting and began walking south through the downtown streets. I had no idea why or where I was walking to instead of just returning to my Jeep. I found myself in the park in front of police headquarters at 12th Street and Locust. I sat on the same bench I had sat on five years prior while waiting for my hiring interview. Everything was exactly the same as I had remembered except the Marine who sat next to me waiting for his interview five years ago was not there now and I was glad to see he was gone. I knew regardless he wouldn't recognize me now if he was still sitting there waiting.

Antonio, Shale and Pancho were powerful, evil and deliberate without remorse of their actions. They killed people and destroyed lives through everything they did and touched.

How did it come to this point? I must have been out of my mind to agree to become "Pancho bait" for the FEDs. How did this get handed off to Tammy Mack and Dewey? We bought crack rocks and bags of weed from people who hid it up their asses.

With an army of federal agents, wire taps, thousands of man-hours of surveillance, the Boxcar team, multi agency this and that, the final answer came down to a request, "Hey, you mind if we try and get these monsters to try and kill you and Tammy? That would really help our case buddy."

I felt my head spin and I was sick to my stomach. I lit a cigarette and clenched my abdominal muscles in an attempt to lesson the cramps in my stomach. I tried to remember the last time I ate but I could not remember when that was or what I had to eat. Maybe after this whole Pancho thing was put to bed, I could settle my nerves and get my appetite back.

I lifted my bony frame from the cement bench, holding my stomach and pointed my feet in the direction of where I had parked the Jeep.

A woman with a child in a stroller walking south through the park towards my bench purposely changed her path of travel to avoid coming near me as I shambled my way north. I was careful not to make eye contact with her to cause her any fear or further discomfort with my cadaverous appearance.

CHAPTER 15 - CHERRY FLAVORED CIGARS

I made it to the Jeep and headed towards Tammy's place to share the news of our new potential forthcoming adventure. It was difficult to forecast her reaction to the task force's request for our assistance.

"What the fuck is wrong with you, Dewey? You look like a ho dog stuffed inside of a dirty hobo sock," Tammy critiqued as I still held my stomach while smoking one of her cigars.

"I don't feel very good today. What do you think of our plan?" asked her.

"I think if you walked into a haunted house, you'd come out with a job application and you got to be out of your God dammed mind playing these games trying to get yourself killed by these bad cops. That isn't your job, Dewey. That man they told you about, Pancho, is the damn bogey man," Tammy loudly scolded.

"It is my job, Tammy, I have to. I can't ask you to do this, anyway," I admitted to her, defeated and realizing asking Tammy to take such an incredible risk with no real payback for the sacrifice wasn't fair to her. She wasn't in my shoes. She wasn't a cop and in the eyes of Shale, she was the disposable lighter waiting to be thrown out. I started to feel guilty for asking her to help me as I had no right to put her at risk.

"Dewey, you couldn't figure out the instructions on a shampoo bottle without my help. We're a team, remember! You're the one who told me that. You giving up now?" she bellowed.

We went back and forth arguing and name calling like scared children until we were able to calm our nerves shaking off the initial shock of what we were contemplating doing.

Tammy was not a sheltered person. She had seen more in her 3 years of life than most people could ever imagine. She had been in thousands of drug houses and seen her share of horrible things to include people being killed. To give credit where credit was due, she had survived on the streets where most people could not have. She was a survivor and wouldn't go down without a fight for anyone.

She knew these men were playing for keeps and killing people was an impersonal business decision for them. She also knew there were no second chances with Shale and his people.

Tammy was a good soul and my friend who had kept me alive to this point. She would never admit her affections for me and I knew she would not let me go in on this alone no matter what I said to her. Our fates whether beaten to death with a hammer or seeing Shale being behind bars were now the same.

FBI agent, Mark Agnello was the lead investigator for the task force and was running everything with little interference from his supervisors. I called Agnello to let him know Tammy was in and we were ready. He thanked me unceremoniously and contacted Netta to instruct her she was clear to do her part.

Netta was delighted with the opportunity to bring down the entire world of the fallen narcs using nothing more than her creative imagination and manipulation. She met with some of the task force agents to rehearse possible scenarios of what to report to Shale that would trigger his immediate employment of Pancho to quell the situation. She was even given a few prop surveillance photos to show Shale.

Netta's body wire recorded her meeting with Shale as another piece of evidence to be used against him and his conspiracy of attempting to murder Tammy and myself. The final piece of evidence needed to demonstrate the furtherance of the act would be Pancho's arrest inside of the house given to Tammy and I by Shale.

The FBI had successfully wired an audio bug in the outdoor patio area behind Red's barbecue under the authority of a lengthy court order. The quality was poor but it did record a partial conversation of Shale talking with Red about their new problem.

Shale called for a Tuesday morning meeting for tip sheets to be drawn amongst the narcs. I knew this was where we would know if Shale had taken the bait or not. Shale would not make the same mistake with Reggie's house. He would have someone anonymously call in the tip from an outside line as was normally done with the others. After Tammy and I were murdered in Shale's trap house, the investigators would invariably pull records of the phone which had provided the tip location. This of course would only lead to a burner cell phone with no identifiable user information.

I was unsure of how Shale would get the tip passed specifically to me without another narc accidentally pulling it from the skull before me. I predicted he would slip it in the skull like a cheap card trick prior to approaching me.

With three other narcs, to include Netta, being the magicians' assistants in the crowd, I was confident I would receive the correct trap house tip sheet without any confusion.

I tried not to react in any way as Shale clumsily did exactly as I had predicted he would. I could see him putting his back to me, fumbling as he was placing a tip sheet into the skull for me to draw next. He approached and allowed me to remove the last remaining piece of paper from the top of the skull's head.

"Hey, Dewey, I want to knock this one out Thursday and it's probably a good idea to take Tammy in there with you," he suggested.

"Not a problem, boss. Tammy and I will knock this out on Thursday," I inexpressively advised him keeping my anger contained.

I looked down at the piece of paper listing the address of "4227 Agnes Ave" as the location of where Tammy and I would be killed shortly after entering. I didn't really care to examine the useless comments listed as they were inconsequential and personally insulting at this point. Tammy and I could knock on the door of the Agnes house dressed in police "Class A" uniforms, which was simply the addition of a formal police hat and black tie to the standard police uniform, and not have any resistance with entering the house.

I picked up Tammy on the way to meet the task force and searched the underside of the Jeep for ticks as instructed. It would be a hindrance to the operation if Shale found Tammy and I talking to guys in tactical cargo pants and sunglasses which was basically a clothing ensemble for every single federal agent in the country with slight variations to the tops.

We repeatedly went over the operational plans, contingency plans and emergency contingency plans to the point it was annoying despite their good intentions to insure our safety.

The task force could not afford to take a single burn with surveillance in the neighborhood around the Agnes house so it was ordered from the top down to stay out of the area until almost the last possible moment when Tammy and I would arrive. It was expected Shale would have Ernie or Anson driving the neighborhoods looking for the FEDs sitting and waiting.

The FEDs had a cleverly disguised small box truck refurbished and prepped as a jump-out vehicle for their tactical raid crew. It was a well worn and older vehicle with company logos on the sides. It blended in seamlessly with the hundreds of other work vehicles driving through the neighborhoods to work sites.

The driver of the Fed's jump-out truck was Gabe, an undercover Kansas State trooper who worked for one of the FBI's gang squads. He weighed close to three hundred pounds and had an impressive wizard-like beard. He was a great undercover and had never been in contact with any of the Super Friends which would allow him to get close to the target house without suspicion even if he was spotted by Shale's lookouts.

We were instructed to wear multiple body wire devices during the operation, in the event one of them failed to transmit a signal, there would be a back up in its place. I protested a bit but it was a non-negotiable topic to the point the operation would be immediately terminated if we refused to wear the devices which were adhered to our underclothing. I tried to not visualize where Tammy had attached her body wire devices as she never wore under garments preferring more comfortable free fitting attire.

The magistrate judge who signed off on the anticipatory warrant for 4227 Agnes Avenue was supportive of the task force's efforts but would not authorize entry and execution of the warrant without additional probable cause of a "triggering" event.

The judge agreed to sign the warrant only if Tammy and I made contact with someone at the door of the Agnes house and were subsequently invited inside of the residence. In the court's opinion, simply standing in front of the door would not be sufficient cause to allow law enforcement to execute the warrant. There needed to be contact with someone at the residence to fulfill the judge's orders.

Tammy and I were comfortable with doing our usual song and dance at the front door as the probability of Pancho killing us on the front porch was unlikely. Tammy and I had a signal prepared for the jump out team. If we were invited inside, Tammy would return to the Jeep with the premise that she had left her lighter there. If the team observed Tammy walking from the Jeep by herself without me, it was the signal to hit the door. If Tammy and I returned to the Jeep together, it was a signal that we were unsuccessful and the operation would be called off.

The day came after a long night of lying in bed staring at the ceiling. I had slept for a couple hours but surprisingly felt more relaxed than tired as I made my way downstairs to prepare for the day. I kept my Dewey crime fighting clothes in a cardboard box in the garage since they were rarely washed and smelled strongly of cigar smoke. My boots were always kept outside of the house as well, as they attracted the grime of the houses I visited at work.

I fastened my ankle holster to the inside of my left leg and placed my small Glock 27 inside of it before pulling the cuff of my jeans over the weapon, concealing it. I had never really looked closely at the weapon issued to me and previously used by several other detectives before me. It looked rough and worn with scratches and light surface oxidation with the metal finish starting to dull. It reminded me of a gun recovered on the streets somewhere used for a Saturday night liquor store robbery or a homicide. I wondered if it had seen any action or if there was any history to it, and if there was, would I really want to know what it had been through. It was not an attractive weapon but it was more reliable than most, which was all that mattered to me.

I loaded a fresh pack of cigarettes in my outer shirt pocket and headed towards the Jeep to head downtown. I kept the day's agenda from my wife erroneously telling her I had a slow day planned at work catching up on paperwork and reports as opposed to telling her I was baiting a serial killer into trying to kill me inside of a drug house. It seemed the right thing to do.

I arrived at Tammy's apartment around seven in the morning and honked the horn to let her know I had arrived. I didn't see Tammy's roommate wave to me as he normally did as she exited the apartment and walked to the Jeep. She opened the door and greeted me with an inaudible mumble I couldn't understand. I was two hours earlier than we normally started our work day and I'm sure she was not happy about having to get up early.

We were scheduled to meet with the task force but not before making our QuikTrip stop for cigars and work beverages to start the day. It was now tradition and a recipe of our success to begin the day with cherry flavored gas station cigars and a couple of beers.

I drove around for thirty minutes to clean myself from any possible surveillance and stopped to look under the vehicle for ticks. When I felt we were clean, I headed towards a location given to me by agent Agnello which was at a small office building in the suburbs of Overland Park.

Agnello was as dry as a martini and never really appeared excited or disappointed to meet anyone regardless of their position. Whether he was ordering a cup of coffee or preparing to execute a high risk warrant, Agnello was a museum painting. I always hoped Tammy would say something off color to him to get a reaction but she was cautiously quiet around him.

Agnello was with two other agents and two FBI technicians who prepared our body wires under our clothing. We discussed the operation for the umpteenth time and Agnello informed us a fixed wing aircraft overhead would be the visual surveillance eye to relay our bust signal to the jump out team.

I placed a call to Shale which was recorded by Agnello using a small hand held audio recorder, "Hey, boss, I picked up Tammy. You want s to head towards Agnes Avenue now?"

"Hey, Dewey, give me thirty minutes and meet me at 54th and Chestnut. There's a church there. I'll meet you in the parking lot. Thanks," hale instructed and disconnected the call before I could respond.

Tammy and I looked at each other. I could feel the blood rushing to my face and my heart racing.

"What's going on, Dewey, this part of the plan?" asked Tammy as he aggressively drew smoke from her cigar.

"I don't know. He's changing something up," I suggested, trying to ide the concern in my voice.

We sat for twenty minutes which seemed much longer by the time hale arrived in an unmarked Crown Victoria. Shale exited his car and alked to the passenger side window to greet Tammy, "Miss Tammy, how re you doing?"

"Good, boss, what's the plan?" she asked with a well held poker ce.

"I just got a call. We hit a deconfliction with the ATF on that Agnes ouse. They've got a gun case with a guy in there. They're working on paper or that door and want to hit it next week. Sorry about that, guys," Shale pologized.

Shale seemed incredibly calm as if he had called off the entire evil aster plan of killing Tammy and myself. Maybe he had come to his senses nd realized the risk was not worth the reward.

"Hey, no problem boss. Tammy's got a spot or two we can work on. e'll heard north and get you an address when we get there," I suggested.

"Actually, an old informant threw me a bone yesterday on a de-nt house, 5138 Bellefountain. A guy there goes by the name "Raj" selling ack and weed," Shale mentioned as he pulled a folded piece of paper from is pocket handing it to Tammy. "We'll follow you over there and I'll have rnie grab the eye for you on the street. You guys are doing great, by the ay, still leading the squad in stats and you know how I like them stats, ammy. Don't forget the rat phone, Dewey."

Tammy gave a forced chuckle as Shale returned to the van. We oked at each other as thoughts raced through our minds. Had Shale been pped off or seen one of the FEDs casing the Agnes house? He was a step ead of us and we were now in a bad spot.

"Fuck Tammy, How do we know if this new spot is the trap house? hat if he called it off just to see if the FEDs kick this door or the Agnes or in? He's baiting us. He must have seen or heard something and now he's waiting for us to make the next move. If we don't knock on this door it's over, he'll be tipped off. Pancho will be in the wind. Maybe he's go people inside the task force?" I wildly speculated, desperate to guess Shale' motives for changing locations.

I called Agnello as I knew he was listening to our body wires an wouldn't need me to explain the situation. The phone didn't ring and wen straight to voicemail. "Mark! Pick up! We're not going to Agnes, he's send ing us to 5138 Bellefountain. Call me back quick and advise. We're a coupl minutes out from the house." I desperately relayed in my message.

It didn't matter, we were out of time, as we had arrived to Belle fountain quicker than expected. We were now faced with two sides o a coin, one side being nothing more than a normal drug house door t knock on as we had done a many times before. The other side of the coi was grainy images replayed in my mind of Reggie lying in the hallway nex to the ladder with his head crushed.

I was sweating profusely now and I rolled the window down as needed to feel the air for a minute. I asked Tammy for one of her cigars an lit it up for a quick drag of the thick flavored smoke.

"All right, Ms. Mack, I'll be back in a few minutes," I assured he while preparing the rat phone.

"We need a story if they ask us how we know each other, Dewey Tammy suggested raising an eyebrow and carefully crafting another eroti Harlequin backstory in her mind.

"We don't need a story because you're not going inside this house I sternly advised her.

"I know, Dewey, how about you want some of this Tammy thang thang but you can't get your freak on unless you smoke. It's like a crack roc is a Viagra pill for you and that lil' softy needs some smoky," she poeticall suggested to me.

"No games, he's in there, Tammy," I interrupted. "Shale beat us, it over. The FEDs are nowhere around. It's just us and this is it. I'm going t step in the doorway and I'm going to just going to blast this Pancho gu the second I see him," I confessed to Tammy while unburdening my con science at the same time.

"That's fine, but I can help with that. Don't turn on the rat phon Trust me. Let's go, Dewey," she instructed.

I removed the pistol from my ankle hostler and placed it in th front of my waistband where I could draw it much quicker to make a sho We slowly exited the Jeep and walked towards the house. The wind picke up a bit as we took in the view of the house from outside of the car. The house was a single story gray bricked structure with a covered porch. It didn't have any of the tell-tale signs of a nuisance house and it was simply just a plain quiet house.

In the corner of my eye, I could see Shale's headlights flash from down the street. I knew he was trying to signal me to turn the rat phone on. "Sorry, Ryan you don't get to hear me getting killed today," I thought to myself.

We reached the porch and walked slowly up the wooden stairs, keeping an eye on the windows for any sign of movement. Tammy gave me a nod as I reached my hand forward to knock on the door.

Lonnie, the young associate of Pancho, slowly opened the door. I refused to put any effort into getting into the house other than just asking for "Raj." Lonnie remained quiet and opened the door wide enough for myself and Tammy to enter. I positioned myself in front of Tammy to prevent her from entering the house first. I placed my hand on the grip of my pistol in my waistband while keeping it concealed under my shirt. As long as Pancho didn't shoot me in the head, I was confident I could get two or three shots off in the initial meeting.

If I encountered Pancho with little distance between us, I could forgo aiming the pistol with both hands and produce reactionary one handed shots from my waist area cutting my draw time down but decreasing accuracy significantly. It was a trade off and not really a good one.

The house was quiet and dim but not dark. Lonnie continued walking speechless towards the interior of the house as we slowly trailed behind him. I decided to draw my pistol from concealment and grip it with both hands preparing for a more accurate shot placement. I was no longer concerned with Lonnie seeing it in my hands as it was silly trying to conceal the weapon at this point. If he was leading me to Pancho, I had no problem with killing him as well in the process, despite his young age.

Lonnie stopped in front of an open door leading into the darkness of an unlit basement. Lonnie glanced at my hands holding the pistol but quickly looked away while pointing his small thin child-finger towards the basement as if this gesture would compel us to follow his silent instructions.

Lonnie's eyes widened in fear as I quickly closed the basement door and turned a deadbolt lock to secure the door in a single fluid motion. The door was not hollow and the frame appeared in solid condition. I knew it would take a few kicks from Pancho to get it open allowing myself plenty of time to place half of the rounds in my magazine into his body. I retreated to the center of the room and positioned myself off center from the door in the event Pancho blindly fired through the door. I took a kneeling position and tightened my grip on my pistol, "Hey, Pancho, it's the police. It's over!"

The sounds of Pancho ascending the stairs were steady and careful as he was most likely cautiously climbing the stairwell in complete darkness.

The intense sudden pain in the back of my head accompanied an equally commensurate sensation of vertigo from the blunt object Lonnie had struck me with. A heavy darkness diminished my hearing and eyesight leaving me unable to cognitively recognize Pancho had forced the door apart and was now standing in the room with us. My pistol was no longer in my hands and I knew it would be difficult to find on the floor until I was collected and on my feet.

I lifted my head enough to see Pancho's legs as he crossed the room towards me. He had a pistol in his hand at his side which he began to raise.

Tammy had decided to join the party at this point landing a crushing blindsided tackle into Pancho that would bring a small tear of joy to any NFL Defensive line coach. We were positioned in a better vantage as Pancho was now without a weapon as well. Somewhere in the room, two pistols were on the floor waiting to be found.

Pancho strained to bring himself to his feet despite Tammy's enormous frame hanging from his back. Pancho was definitely a special forces soldier in his prime with incredible strength and stamina for his size.

Tammy and I landed strikes as hard as we could into his head and torso, some of which he countered and returned with much more accurate and devastating power. He paced himself like a boxer knowing he could outlast us while we were wildly expending our energy.

I caught Pancho forgoing opportunities to land counter strikes choosing instead to scan the room for one of the pistols on the floor. We had to keep him on the ropes until I got to a pistol first.

I engaged Pancho in a low grappling move grabbing his legs allowing Tammy enough time to swing a lamp catching him in the bridge of his nose, breaking it. It was an incredibly lucky strike but not enough to bring him down.

Pancho gave up looking for a gun and focused on landing harder strikes into Tammy and myself. Pancho was slowing in his movements but was using more strength when he did make contact. He was outpacing us and beating us senseless in the process. We were losing and it would only be a few more minutes until he moved to the main event of taking back possession of his firearm.

Pancho's legs crumpled beneath his body as a single gunshot discharged from behind me. The round from my pistol now in Lonnie's hand had missed its intended target instead passing through Pancho's stomach and severing his spine above his hips.

Pancho held his stomach and was positioned oddly on the floor as if sitting down to relax for a few minutes with his legs formed in a circle in front of him.

Lonnie was no longer Pancho's promising apprentice of death but instead, but now a scared kid with tears in his eyes. He let the weapon fall to the floor as he ran from the house through the back yard leading to an alley.

I quickly took possession of both firearms from the floor and inventoried the injuries to myself and Tammy. Tammy had lost several teeth and my right hand suffered a "boxer" fracture to my outside knuckle which was depressed. My hand was swelling and I was incapable of using it without intense pain. Our faces were starting to show the early stages of bruising and swelling.

The rat phone was vibrating in my pocket and I knew who was on the line. "You should come in here, boss. We got him," I hoarsely whispered into the phone between coughs of pain.

"Dewey, your phone wasn't dialed in. We lost the ear. What's going on? You all right?" Shale asked.

"We caught the guy who killed Reggie, boss." I replied.

"Just wait there, I'm coming in," Shale advised.

Shale entered through the back of the house holding his firearm in a low ready position with both hands and scanning the room for threats until he was standing over Pancho.

"Hey Ryan next time you want to kill Tammy and me, you're just going to have to do it yourself," I quipped with a flippant smile.

Shale finished Pancho with a contact head shot entering the top of his skull and exiting from the bottom his face removing close to half of his lower mandible. It was rather gruesome and enough of a shock to allow Shale to get the drop on Tammy and I, "Drop the guns, Dewey, now!"

I allowed the weapons to fall to the floor as my right hand was now useless anyway. Shale kicked the weapons further away from Tammy and I and then closed and secured the back door of the house.

"The show's over. The FEDs are coming, all of them. They know all about you and your play time rip crew. This is the part where you finally make a good decision," I warned.

"Yeah, you're not that smart, Dewey. You're bluffing, no one showed up to the other spot. It's just us. All right, both of you, let's go downstairs," he ordered.

"Sorry boss, lesson one, basements are where people go to die, boss," I politely declined.

"People die in a lot of places, Dewey," he exclaimed in a calm quiet voice.

I could read his mind. He was on the edge of deciding whether to kill myself and Tammy. He was working the nerve to up to do it which was immeasurably more difficult than having Antonio and Pancho do it for him.

"These wires makin' my titties itch, Dewey," Tammy complained.

I could see fear in Shale's eyes for the first time, "Yeah, these are kind of uncomfortable. I thought the FEDs would have something better," I critiqued.

Tammy and I slowly pulled our shirts up to expose our torsos and the devices that were taped to our bodies.

Shale walked to a window and looked through a sliver of space in the blinds. He could now see a regatta of vehicles positioning outside for a barricaded gunman operation. He stepped back from the window and walked to the other side of the room where he retrieved my pistol from the floor.

Shale casually sat on the sofa in a relaxed position, running his hand over the top of his head smoothing his hair, "Here you go, Dewey." Shale held out my pistol in his hand with the barrel pointing towards himself to show he was genuinely returning the item to its rightful owner. It was a surreal moment watching Shale comfortably seated on the couch immediately to the side of Pancho's violently destroyed body.

I purposely moved in slow exaggerated movements as I cautiously took the weapon from his outstretched hand. He maintained a grip on his own service weapon, which he kept at his side, resting on the couch next to his leg.

"You kids did great today. You caught the bad guys. All right, head on out you two, I'll clean up here and join you in a minute. We'll debrief on this in the morning at the office. I'm writing a letter of commendation to the chief first thing in the morning, Dewey. Tammy, you're going to get a little something extra in your pay bucket, too. But don't get too relaxed guys, we got to knock down a lot more houses to make quota this month. That's what the chief wants," Shale expressed with a dazed look in his eyes.

"You can make this a better situation, boss. Just leave the gun and let's walk out together very slowly" I pleaded.

Shale waved his pistol in a sweeping motion for Tammy and I to leave him alone, "You two kids go home. You've had a long day. Tammy, you got one of those cigars?"

Tammy removed a crumpled box from her sweatpants pocket and surprisingly found a cigar still mostly intact even after the Pancho altercation. After searching for a minute, Tammy found a lighter on the floor and handed to Shale for him to light the cigar.

"Cherry flavored? Very nice, Tammy," Shale complimented as he slowly drew smoke from the cigar.

I wanted to plead again with Shale to reconsider and come outside with us but Tammy wisely and gently placed her arm on my shoulder, "Let's go, Dewey."

He stared across the room, looking through the rising smoke of his cigar with little expression on his face.

We placed our hands in the air and slowly walked out of the house towards the large crowd of agents and law enforcement personnel.

Agnello almost seemed to smile as we reached him but perhaps it was just a shadow across his face that gave that appearance. The anticlimactic and muffled sound of Shale's gun discharging from inside the house was neither surprising nor alarming to Tammy and I.

After the investigation had concluded, Shale's service weapon was returned to the department armory where it was cleaned by Randy and anonymously re-issued to a graduating probationary police officer from the next academy class.

The take-down operation was successful with all defendants being arrested without further incidents. Only one of the defendants in the indictment went to trial and subsequently lost. The cases were quickly pled with defendants bargaining for the best deals they could through their attorneys. Ernie received 18 years and Anson received 12.

Netta left SNU and went to work for Sgt. Benedict's squad and was later promoted to Sergeant with service in various other departments to include Homicide and Robbery.

Tammy and I returned to our separate worlds never to see each other again. She was identified in the reports of investigation and affidavits only as "SNU Informant # 3071" without any reference to her real name, Tamera Josephine Mack.

She worked with Netta for a few more cases but her health declined and she retired from her adventures on the streets.

Tammy passed away five years later. She was indigent and was buried by the state of Missouri. There was no memorial, no service nor mention of her passing in the newspaper. No flowers were left on her grave, only a few boxes of cherry flavored cigars were left on her headstone from time to time.

It has been 18 years since I worked side by side with my friend and mentor, Tammy Josephine Mack. I can still vividly remember her stories, inappropriate jokes, her laugher and mispronunciations of my name. She taught me all people have a valuable purpose for entering your life and although it may not be known to you at that time, perhaps later in life it will be revealed with clearer purpose.

I am thankful for my friend who watched over me and lighted our path on the darkest of journeys. We entered the hardest of doors for the uninvited. We were only able to stay for a few brief moments with the people inside of the quiet houses but we left them with smiles on their faces.

THE END

ABOUT THE AUTHOR

Jeff transitioned to law enforcement after finding himself unemployed from his comfortable suburban job as a graphic artist. In 2003, Jeff spent a year undercover as a street junky visiting violent drug houses throughout Kansas City alongside his informant, Tamera Josephine Mack, a boisterous, street-wise African American woman. Together they knocked on hundreds of doors attempting to gain entry to purchase drugs from within.

Their contentious friendship was built from the necessity of survival in a sea of lost souls and dangerous men.

Almost two decades later, Jeff is currently a DEA Special Agent in Detroit, Michigan. Jeff's New York Times interview regarding his arrest of the world's oldest and most successful cartel mule, Leo Sharp became the basis for Clint Eastwood's movie, The Mule where Leo was portrayed by Clint Eastwood and Jeff was portrayed by Bradley Cooper.

FOR FURTHER INFORMATION VISIT
WWW.ALLESTONEPRODUCTIONS.COM

Printed in Great Britain
by Amazon

17069975R00098